# Laboratory Management and Safety

## IN THE SCIENCE CLASSROOM

Mc Graw Hill | Glencoe McGraw-Hill

New York, New York    Columbus, Ohio    Woodland Hills, California    Peoria, Illinois

**Photo Credits:**
Cover: Bob Daemmrich Photography; **30** (both) Matt Meadows Photography; **31** (all) Glencoe; **32** Glencoe; **33** (both) Courtesy Sargent-Welch/VWR Scientific Products; **34** Courtesy Sargent-Welch/VWR Scientific Products

*Glencoe/McGraw-Hill*

*A Division of The McGraw-Hill Companies*

Send all inquiries to:
Glencoe/McGraw-Hill
8787 Orion Place
Columbus, OH 43240

ISBN 0-07-825454-X
Printed in the United States of America
13 14 15   009   10 09 08 07

# Table of Contents

# Using This Manual

## About Glencoe's Science Laboratory and Field Activities

Glencoe Science has laboratory activities designed to make it easy for you to plan and facilitate them in your classrooms and in the field. Many of the activities use common, inexpensive materials. The activities are clearly presented, with numbered steps and illustrations. The hands-on activities are varied in design—from short to long, from directed to open-ended. The general organization of the activities is described on p. 17.

All laboratory activities have been thoroughly reviewed by several safety experts. All full-length labs in the Student Editions have been bench tested to ensure quality and safety. All Mini-LABS have been teacher tested.

## About This Manual

This Manual provides basic information about lab and field management and safety. It is intended to help you foster students' confidence regarding their laboratory and field skills and a life-long interest in science. Preparedness promotes safety in your classroom, laboratory, and during science fieldwork. This preparedness should be for all students, including those confined to wheelchairs, on crutches, or those who may have allergies to substances found in a laboratory or field setting.

Glencoe/McGraw-Hill makes NO claims to the completeness of this manual and its discussion of laboratory and field safety, chemical storage, and first aid. The material presented is not all-inclusive nor does it address all of the hazards associated with handling, storage, and disposal of chemicals or with laboratory management.

The disposal of chemicals is strictly regulated by local, state, and federal laws. Consult these laws before attempting to dispose of any chemicals. See pp. 84 and 129–130 for guidelines for the handling and disposal of chemicals. The following resource provides more information about handling and disposing of chemicals: *Prudent Practices in the Laboratory: Handling and Disposal of Chemicals.* Washington, DC: National Academy Press, 1995.

> **Current state and local regulations regarding laboratory safety supercede this manual.**

## Safety Issues

Laboratory and field experiences should not be denied because of reluctance to take risks—the risks can be minimized with knowledge and careful planning. The actions of one person affect the safety and well being of others in the same room/building. Safety plays a major role in all areas of our lives—at home, at work, during sports and recreational activities, on the road, and in the products we choose to use. We take these safety measures in stride. Laboratory and field safety should be treated in the same way. It should be part and parcel of every laboratory activity.

## Safety Sources

This manual is based on guidelines from various state departments of education and a number of organizations and agencies concerned with safety. It provides reasons for safety—to show that authoritative sources should be consulted if you are not sure how the equipment you have works or what steps you need to take to respond appropriately to emergency situations. Several position papers provide safety guidelines for laboratory situations.

- **American Academy of Ophthalmology:** *The Use of Contact Lenses in an Industrial Environment*
- **Council of State Science Supervisors:** *Laboratory Safety; Science Education Safety: Key Issues in School Laboratory Safety; The Use of Human Body Fluids and Tissue Products in Biology Teaching*
- **National Biology Teachers Association:** *Role of Laboratory and Field Instruction in Biology Education; The Use of Animals in Biology Education; The Use of Human Fluids and Tissue Products in Teaching Biology*
- **National Science Teachers Association:** *Guidelines for Responsible Use of Animals in the Classroom; Elementary School Science; Laboratory Science; Liability of Teachers for Laboratory Safety and Field Trips*

Log on to the Glencoe Web site at **science.glencoe.com** for links to the agencies that sponsored these papers and to access Material Safety Data Sheets (MSDS)(see pp. 117–121). Insert phone numbers on p. 10 for local agencies that can be contacted for information, such as the Poison Control Center, The American Red Cross, and so forth.

## How This Manual Is Organized

This manual is organized according to various teacher and administrative responsibilities related to different situations during a science course.

- **Introducing/Reviewing Laboratory Safety Guidelines** [pp. 11–16] pertains to procedures appropriate at the beginning of a course. This section presents guidelines for the teacher and suggestions for student safe conduct. Blackline masters are included to aid in the presentation of guidelines to students—safety symbols, student safety guidelines, and a sample student science laboratory safety contract.
- **Introducing/Reviewing Laboratory Work** [pp. 17–80] provides an introduction to Glencoe science lab activities in which safety symbols and warning statements are discussed. It also provides an overview of lab equipment and techniques and procedures for using laboratory devices and materials (see pp. 17–23). Blackline masters of worksheets are included that may be used to help students practice their lab techniques and skills or to assess students' readiness for lab work (see pp. 29–80). Answers to the worksheets appear on pp. 24–28.

- **Managing the Laboratory Day-by-Day** [pp. 81–89] presents material about managing a laboratory/classroom on a daily basis. It covers preparation, pre-lab activities, supervision during the laboratory activity, post-activity procedures, and laboratory cleanup.
- **Responding to Emergencies** [pp. 91–104] concerns emergency response guidelines. These procedures should be augmented by training in first aid and in handling emergency equipment. Blackline Masters are provided for sample medical emergency and accident report forms.
- **Managing Lab Work Outside the Classroom** [pp. 105–116] pertains to home lab assignments and science field work. Basic procedures plus sample letters to parents and guardians and a sample field trip permission form are included.
- **Managing Laboratory Materials Storage** [pp.117–130] includes information on Material Safety Data Sheets (MSDS) and the storage and handling of chemicals, radioactive substances, biological specimens, and live animals. The section also deals with inventory practices and suggests ways to get rid of old and unnecessary substances.
- **Preparing Live Exhibits** [pp. 131–132] gives instructions for preparing aquariums and terrariums and for growing plants for observation.
- **Checking Facilities and Equipment** [pp. 133–144] contains information vital to planning, usually conducted by teachers and administrators at a time when equipment needs are considered. This section discusses issues that should be addressed when updating your facilities and equipment—renovations and new construction. Issues include space requirements, facility design, safety equipment specifications, and safety requirements for various types of investigation equipment. Also see the list below of suppliers for science laboratory equipment and materials.

## Science Materials Supplier List

**Carolina Biological Supply Company**
2700 York Road
Burlington, NC 27215
800-334-5551
www.carolina.com

**Fisher Scientific Educational**
485 South Frontage Road
Burr Ridge, IL 60521
800-955-1177
www.fisheredu.com

**Fisher Scientific Company**
4500 Turnberry Drive
Hanover Park, IL 60103
800-766-7000
www.fishersci.com

**Flinn Scientific**
P.O. Box 219
770 North Raddant Road
Batavia, IL 60510
800-452-1261
www.flinnsci.com

**Frey Scientific**
100 Paragon Road
Mansfield, OH 44903
800-225-3739
www.freyscientific.com

**Sargent-Welch/Cenco**
P.O. Box 5229
911 Commerce Court
Buffalo Grove, IL 60089
800-727-4368
www.sargentwelch.com

**Science Kit & Boreal Laboratories**
777 East Park Drive
Tonawanda, NY 14150
800-828-7777
www.sciencekit.com

**Ward's Natural Science Establishment, Inc.**
P.O. Box 92912
5100 Henrietta Road
Rochester, NY 14692
800-962-2660
www.wardsci.com

# Phone List for Local Resources

- **EMERGENCIES: 911**

- Fire Department _____

- Water Treatment Facility _____

- Poison Control Center _____

- Hazmat _____

- Hospitals _____

  _____

  _____

  _____

- American Red Cross _____

- School District Office _____

- Other: _____

  _____

  _____

# Introducing/Reviewing Laboratory Safety Guidelines

## Safe Laboratory Conduct

Whether you are a first-time or very experienced teacher, a review of safety guidelines is in order. This section deals with behaviors and actions that foster a safe learning environment. Because you serve as the role model for the behavior in the laboratory that you expect from your students, first review the safety guidelines for teachers. Then, on the first day of classes, introduce or review the safety guidelines that are the students' responsibility.

## Teacher Safety Guidelines

- Thoroughly review your local safety regulations and this manual. Modify any activities to comply with your local regulations. For example, open flames are NOT permitted in some states or communities.

- Be trained in first aid and CPR.

- Be aware of students with allergies or other medical conditions that might limit their activities or require special protective equipment, such as facemasks.

- Have a list of substances to be used in lab activities made available to the doctor of any pregnant teacher or student so that limitations may be determined beforehand.

- NEVER leave students unattended in the classroom or field setting.

- NEVER be alone or out of earshot of someone when you prepare lab activities or equipment.

- Always wash your hands with antibacterial soap and warm water upon entering the laboratory, after live cultures have been handled, after cleanup, and before removing safety goggles.

- NEVER perform an investigation on any animal that might be a health hazard to humans or cause pain or suffering to the animal.

- Use protista and other invertebrates for lab or field activities involving animals when possible. Protista represent a wide variety of organisms and can be obtained in large quantities.

- A qualified adult supervisor who has had training in the proper care and handling of laboratory animals must assume responsibility for the conditions of any activity that involves living vertebrates. NO activity/investigation should be conducted that involves drugs, organisms pathogenic to humans or other vertebrates, ionizing radiation, surgical procedures, or carcinogens unless the procedures have been approved by and will be performed or supervised by a qualified biomedical scientist.

- Have students notify you beforehand if they plan to bring in a pet for observation. See p. 128 regarding precautions for such events.

**Safety Guidelines**

- Instruct students about the hazards involved with wild animals and your school's policy and local and state laws regarding their capture and use in the classroom/laboratory. **WARNING:** *Wild animals may exhibit unpredictable behaviors, may become dangerous as they mature, and if declawed, may not be accepted by zoos and will probably die if released into the wild.* **WARNING:** *There is the potential of contracting rabies from any infected warm-blooded animal.*

- It is recomended that you purchase fumigated, steam sterilized materials. **WARNING:**

  - *Owl pellets can be a source of salmonella.*

  - *Bird nests contain many organisms that can cause diseases.*

  - *Bird eggs, even if disinfected when first acquired, will decay after a few days from gases building up in them. Rotten eggs produce noxious odors.*

  - *Some insects carry diseases that are serious if transmitted to humans.*

## Presenting Safety Guidelines to Students

- Review the use and location of safety equipment, evacuation guidelines, and first aid procedures. Refer to fire drill regulations and a chart of emergency procedures, which should be posted in a prominent place in the laboratory. Assign safety partners and explain their role in helping during emergencies.

- Discuss safe disposal of materials and laboratory cleanup policy.

- Preview Glencoe science activities with students and discuss the safety icons and their meanings (see p. 17). Point out the warning statements and the importance of heeding them. Distribute the Safety Symbols reference sheet (see p. 14).

- Distribute and discuss Student Laboratory and Safety Guidelines (see p. 15). Emphasize proper attitudes for working in the laboratory and field and review or present school rules regarding the consequences of misbehavior. Stress the need for safe practices on the part of everyone involved. Then distribute the Student Science Laboratory Safety Contract found on p. 16. You may wish to have each student and parent or guardian sign a safety contract at the beginning of each course. Review the safety guidelines and safety contract with students at least once a month.

## Blackline Masters Divider

# SAFETY SYMBOLS

| SAFETY SYMBOLS | HAZARD | EXAMPLES | PRECAUTION | REMEDY |
|---|---|---|---|---|
| **DISPOSAL** | Special disposal procedures need to be followed. | certain chemicals, living organisms | Do not dispose of these materials in the sink or trash can. | Dispose of wastes as directed by your teacher. |
| **BIOLOGICAL** | Organisms or other biological materials that might be harmful to humans | bacteria, fungi, blood, unpreserved tissues, plant materials | Avoid skin contact with these materials. Wear mask or gloves. | Notify your teacher if you suspect contact with material. Wash hands thoroughly. |
| **EXTREME TEMPERATURE** | Objects that can burn skin by being too cold or too hot | boiling liquids, hot plates, dry ice, liquid nitrogen | Use proper protection when handling. | Go to your teacher for first aid. |
| **SHARP OBJECT** | Use of tools or glassware that can easily puncture or slice skin | razor blades, pins, scalpels, pointed tools, dissecting probes, broken glass | Practice common-sense behavior and follow guidelines for use of the tool. | Go to your teacher for first aid. |
| **FUME** | Possible danger to respiratory tract from fumes | ammonia, acetone, nail polish remover, heated sulfur, moth balls | Make sure there is good ventilation. Never smell fumes directly. Wear a mask. | Leave foul area and notify your teacher immediately. |
| **ELECTRICAL** | Possible danger from electrical shock or burn | improper grounding, liquid spills, short circuits, exposed wires | Double-check setup with teacher. Check condition of wires and apparatus. | Do not attempt to fix electrical problems. Notify your teacher immediately. |
| **IRRITANT** | Substances that can irritate the skin or mucus membranes of the respiratory tract | pollen, moth balls, steel wool, fiber glass, potassium permanganate | Wear dust mask and gloves. Practice extra care when handling these materials. | Go to your teacher for first aid. |
| **CHEMICAL** | Chemicals that can react with and destroy tissue and other materials | bleaches such as hydrogen peroxide; acids such as sulfuric acid, hydrochloric acid; bases such as ammonia, sodium hydroxide | Wear goggles, gloves, and an apron. | Immediately flush the affected area with water and notify your teacher. |
| **TOXIC** | Substance may be poisonous if touched, inhaled, or swallowed | mercury, many metal compounds, iodine, poinsettia plant parts | Follow your teacher's instructions. | Always wash hands thoroughly after use. Go to your teacher for first aid. |
| **OPEN FLAME** | Open flame may ignite flammable chemicals, loose clothing, or hair | alcohol, kerosene, potassium permanganate, hair, clothing | Tie back hair. Avoid wearing loose clothing. Avoid open flames when using flammable chemicals. Be aware of locations of fire safety equipment. | Notify your teacher immediately. Use fire safety equipment if applicable. |

 **Eye Safety**
Proper eye protection should be worn at all times by anyone performing or observing science activities.

 **Clothing Protection**
This symbol appears when substances could stain or burn clothing.

 **Animal Safety**
This symbol appears when safety of animals and students must be ensured.

 **Radioactivity**
This symbol appears when radioactive materials are used.

# Student Laboratory and Safety Guidelines

## Regarding Emergencies

- Inform the teacher immediately of *any* mishap—fire, injury, glassware breakage, chemical spills, and so forth.
- Follow your teacher's instructions and your school's procedures in dealing with emergencies.

## Regarding Your Person

- Do NOT wear clothing that is loose enough to catch on anything and avoid sandals or open-toed shoes.
- Wear protective safety gloves, goggles, and aprons as instructed.
- Always wear safety goggles (not glasses) when using hazardous chemicals.
- Wear goggles throughout entire activity, cleanup, and handwashing.
- Keep your hands away from your face while working in the laboratory.
- Remove synthetic fingernails before working in the lab (these are highly flammable).
- Do NOT use hair spray, mousse, or other flammable hair products just before or during laboratory work where an open flame is used (they can ignite easily).
- Tie back long hair and loose clothing to keep them away from flames and equipment.
- Remove loose jewelry—chains or bracelets—while doing lab work.
- NEVER eat or drink while in the lab or store food in lab equipment or the lab refrigerator.
- Do NOT inhale vapors or taste, touch, or smell any chemical or substance unless instructed to do so by your teacher.

## Regarding Your Work

- Read all instructions before you begin a laboratory or field activity. Ask questions if you do not understand any part of the activity.
- Work ONLY on activities assigned by your teacher.
- Do NOT substitute other chemicals/substances for those listed in your activity.
- Do NOT begin any activity until directed to do so by your teacher.
- Do NOT handle any equipment without specific permission.
- Remain in your own work area unless given permission by your teacher to leave it.
- Do NOT point heated containers—test tubes, flasks, and so forth—at yourself or anyone else.
- Do NOT take any materials or chemicals out of the classroom.
- Stay out of storage areas unless you are instructed to be there and are supervised by your teacher.
- NEVER work alone in the laboratory.
- When using dissection equipment, always cut away from yourself and others. Cut downward, never stabbing at the object.
- Handle living organisms or preserved specimens only when authorized by your teacher.
- Always wear heavy gloves when handling animals. If you are bitten or stung, notify your teacher immediately.

## Regarding Cleanup

- Keep work and lab areas clean, limiting the amount of easily ignitable materials.
- Turn off all burners and other equipment before leaving the lab.
- Carefully dispose of waste materials as instructed by your teacher.
- Wash your hands thoroughly with soap and warm water after each activity.

# *Student Science Laboratory Safety Contract*

## I agree to:

- Act responsibly at all times in the laboratory.

- Follow all instructions given, orally or in writing, by my teacher.

- Perform only those activities assigned and approved by my teacher.

- Protect my eyes, face, hands, and body by wearing proper clothing and using protective equipment provided by my school.

- Carry out good housekeeping practices as instructed by my teacher.

- Know the location of safety and first aid equipment in the laboratory.

- Notify my teacher immediately of an emergency.

- NEVER work alone in the laboratory.

- NEVER eat or drink in the laboratory unless instructed to do so by my teacher.

- Handle living organisms or preserved specimens only when authorized by my teacher, and then, with respect.

- NEVER enter or work in a supply area unless instructed to do so and supervised by my teacher.

**[This portion of the contract is to be kept by the student.]**

------------------------------------------------------------------------------------------------

**[Return this portion to your teacher.]**

I, _____, [print name] have read each of the statements in the Student Science Laboratory Safety Contract and understand these safety rules. I agree to abide by the safety regulations and any additional written or verbal instructions provided by the school district or my teacher. I further agree to follow all other written and verbal instructions given in class.

_____        _____
Student Signature                                                    Date

I acknowledge that my child/ward has signed this contract in good faith.

_____        _____
Parent/Guardian Signature                                        Date

# Introducing/Reviewing Laboratory Work

Following proper techniques when using laboratory equipment helps prevent accidents and cuts down on the cost of replacement materials and devices. Students' success also is increased as their familiarity with the devices and their measurement and analysis skills increase. To facilitate student success in the classroom laboratory, first familiarize yourself with the general organization of Glencoe's science activities. The organization varies according to the type of activity. Then orient the students to the laboratory setting. This includes reviewing equipment and correct handling procedures with them, the use of SI units in their activities, and assessing their readiness for work in the laboratory.

## Organization of *Glencoe* Science Laboratory Activities

- An **introductory statement** explains the science concepts involved in the activity. Specific information for the investigation of the problem is re-emphasized. This statement appears under the investigation title.
- A **strategy** or **objectives** provides objectives for student performance. If the student does not understand the goal(s) of the activity, a rereading of the section is advised.
- **Materials** is the list of all materials or possible materials needed for the activity. The **Materials** section should be previewed so that any supplies to be contributed by students may be obtained in advance. Be sure to assemble these materials *before* the beginning of a class period.
- A **safety precautions** section provides **icons** to prompt safety awareness and general **warning statement(s)** pertinent to the activity.
- Some activities include a section that states the **problem** or **what will be investigated**.
- Some activities have students state a **hypothesis**.
- **Procedure** is the step-by-step set of instructions for the activity. You may want to discuss the procedure with students before they begin the activity. Pre-activity discussions help prevent misuse of equipment and injuries that can result from careless use of the glassware, burners, and/or corrosive chemicals. Specific **safety warning statements** are placed appropriately in the **Procedure** section.
- **Data and Observations** includes sample graphs, charts, and tables to help improve student analysis skills. Emphasis should be placed on the need to record all observations during and at the completion of the activity. In many cases, recorded data provide the necessary link in cause and effect relationships. Each student should do his or her own computations except in those activities where group work or class averages are required.
- An **analysis** or **questions and conclusions** section contains discussion questions and blanks for student answers at the end of each activity. These questions are designed to review main ideas, to direct attention to key parts of the procedure, and to relate the material to science concepts and applications. Answering these questions promotes and reinforces student learning.
- A **strategy check** or **hypothesis check** section allows students to evaluate the activity. If a student can place a checkmark in the blank provided, he or she has gained a skill, interpreted a concept, or learned a process.
- **Going further, extension and applications,** and **further investigations** is a section in some of the science activities. Students are directed to extend the activity or to research a related topic.

Lab Techniques

# Overview of Laboratory Equipment

Distribute to students the visual overview of basic Laboratory Equipment found on pp. 30–34 of this manual. Identify the various devices and explain their uses. Have students write in the names of the devices/parts on the lines provided. (The names of the devices/parts are listed on p. 24 of this manual.) Especially stress the importance of knowing the parts of a microscope.

# Safe Laboratory Techniques and Procedures

Review the following material on general laboratory techniques. Discuss the information with students, and at the appropriate times, demonstrate to students the techniques for using laboratory equipment and materials properly.

### Using Heat Sources

- Use smooth-surface hot plates as a heat source when possible, especially if any flammable liquid is involved. Clean the plate surface after each use as soon as it has cooled. **WARNING:** *Hot plates should be placed out of reach to avoid accidental contact.*
- Hot plate thermostats should be set at the correct temperature for the experiment—NOT on the maximum temperature.
- Alcohol burners are NOT recommended. If you must use them, check for cracks or chips and fill prior to student use. Use a plastic squeeze-type bottle to refill with alcohol or burner fuel, making sure the burner has cooled before adding fuel. Add a pinch of salt to pure alcohol in the burner so the flame may be seen. Be sure a fire extinguisher is nearby. **WARNING:** *Many duplicating fluids contain heavy metals, such as lead compounds, and are NOT recommended for use in alcohol burners due to by-products produced from burning.* Ask for a Material Safety Data Sheet (MSDS [see pp. 117–121]) from the supplier of the duplicating fluid to verify purity if this fluid is to be used.
- Match the burner to the type of gas available (i.e. natural, artificial, or L.P. gas).
- Sparkers or strikers are recommended for lighting burners. **WARNING:** *Matches tend to litter the lab as well as pose a fire hazard if not properly handled.*
- Gas burners should be operated at a sensibly low level.
- Hot water baths should NOT be boiled unless absolutely necessary.
- NEVER leave an open flame unattended. When a burner is not in use, turn it off.
- Do NOT reach across an open flame.
- Light bulbs used in experiments should be the lowest wattage possible.

### Heating Objects/Substances

- Use a hot plate, rather than a gas burner, when evaporating liquids.
- Objects should NOT be held for an excessive period of time in a gas-burner flame.
- Always point the open end of a test tube away from yourself and others. **WARNING:** *Some chemicals can boil out of the test tube violently and unexpectedly when being heated.*
- Heat-generating chemicals should be mixed slowly.
- NEVER heat chemicals in a closed container such as a corked test tube. **WARNING:** *The expanding gas inside will cause the test tube to explode or turn the stopper into a projectile with considerable force.*

- Do NOT use bare hands to pick up a container that has been heated or hand a heated container to someone. Hold the back of your hand near the container and check for heat. If you can feel heat, use a mitten or tongs to pick up the container.
- NEVER reach across a hot apparatus to perform an experiment. The apparatus should be placed so that if hot liquids are spilled, they will fall on the laboratory table, not on a person.
- Heated objects should be attended to constantly or placed where they are shielded from accidental contact.
- Limit air flow from open doors and windows when working with flammables.
- Limit the quantity of flammable and combustible chemicals in the work area to the amount actually needed. For example, do NOT leave the can of alcohol nearby after filling burners.

### Using Electrical Apparatuses

- Make sure that all electrical cords are in good condition, not frayed. **WARNING:** *Do NOT use any electrical equipment that needs repair.*
- Make sure that circuits are NOT overloaded.
- Turn off all power sources when setting up circuits or repairing equipment.
- Check all circuits set up by students before the power is turned on.
- When assembling circuits, connect the live portion last. When disassembling, disconnect the live portion first.
- Do NOT use metal articles such as rulers or metal pencils or writing pens, or wear metal jewelry when working with electrical equipment.
- When disconnecting electrical equipment, pull from the plug and NOT the cord.
- Use caution when handling electrical equipment that has been in use. The equipment may be warm or hot from being used.
- NEVER connect, disconnect, or operate a piece of electrical equipment with wet hands or while standing on a wet floor.
- Use precautions to prevent spills on electric equipment or electrical outlets.

### Working with Chemicals

- Work carefully with oxidizing agents. **WARNING:** *Chlorates, nitrates, or peroxides and other oxidizers should NOT contact combustible substances.*
- Discard any glove with holes or cracks. **WARNING**: *Chemicals can diffuse through a glove, increasing exposure when the glove holds the chemical against the skin.*
- When removing gloves, peel the gloves off your hand, starting at the wrists and working toward the fingers. Keep the outside surface of the gloves from touching the skin during removal.
- Match the correct glove to the substance to be used. Refer to the labels on the glove boxes. **WARNING:** *Certain gloves can dissolve when they are in contact with solvent.*
- Use extra precaution with acids and bases. **WARNING:** *Always pour acid into water. Do NOT pour water into acids.*
- Remember to wash an acid or base immediately from your skin.
- Use a pipette bulb. NEVER pipette liquids using your mouth.
- Read labels twice before using any chemical.
- Do NOT pour extra chemicals back into the original containers. This causes contamination of the chemicals and may cause incorrect results to occur in future investigations.

- NEVER use the same spatula to remove chemicals from two different containers. Each container should have its own spatula.
- When removing a stopper from a bottle, do NOT lay it down on the lab table, but place the stopper between two fingers and hold the bottle so that the label is in the palm of your hand. Both the bottle and the stopper will be held in one hand. (See p. 46 and pp. 50–51.)
- Replace all stoppers and caps on the correct bottles as soon as you have finished using them.
- Demonstration of a volcano with ammonium dichromate should be performed by an experienced adult under a fume hood or outside with the students standing upwind. Protective equipment MUST be worn. **WARNING:** *Ammonium dichromate produces chromium (III) oxide, a carcinogen.*

## Working with Minerals

- Identifying minerals by tasting should be avoided. **WARNING:** *Tasting of any substance is NOT recommended. Even if the substance is safe, the container likely is not. Some semimetals, such as arsenic, antimony, and allemontite, are poisonous.*
- In the event you work with uranium ores, minimize risks by using the smallest sample for the shortest amount of time possible. **WARNING:** *AVOID direct contact with the ore—use tongs or forceps and sealed samples.*

## Using Thermometers

- NEVER hold the thermometer bulb in an open flame.
- Use only non-mercury thermometers with metal coating in an oven.
- Wrap a strip of tape around round thermometers, leaving a protruding piece, to keep them from rolling off work surfaces.

## Using Batteries

- Check batteries to be sure they are charged.
- Check batteries to be sure they are not leaking. Dispose of all leaking batteries. (See p. 83 regarding the safe disposal of batteries.)
- Clean with soap and water all places a leaking battery has contaminated.
- **WARNING:** *Do NOT try to recharge any battery not specifically designed to be recharged. An explosion may result.*
- **WARNING:** *Do NOT try to heat a battery to make it work better. It may explode.*
- **WARNING:** *Do NOT store batteries in drawers where they may roll around loosely. The rolling action may cause the batteries to spring leaks.*

## Using Lasers

- The laser beam should be at waist level or below whenever possible.
- Use laser goggles and disinfect them after use. (See pp. 84–85 and 138.)
- NEVER point the laser at anyone.
- NEVER stare at the laser beam or view reflected beams.
- Block off the beam past the target (a sheet of rough wood or a flat piece of carbon available at industrial lighting stores works well). The target or any objects in the beam area should be nonreflective.
- NEVER leave the laser unattended. Prevent unauthorized access.
- Be sure the laser cord is grounded.
- Set up prisms and mirrors in advance to avoid unexpected reflections when using a laser. Avoid other accidental reflections when using a laser by removing jewelry, wall mirrors, and so forth.

## Using Centrifuges

- Make sure the centrifuge is securely anchored where its vibrations will not cause bottles or equipment to fall.
- Always close the centrifuge lid during use.
- Do NOT leave a running centrifuge until full operating speed is reached and the machine is running smoothly without excess vibration.
- Immediately stop the centrifuge if vibration occurs. Check that tubes are loaded symmetrically and contain approximately the same amounts of liquid.
- Regularly clean the buckets, centrifuge tube cushions, and rotors. **WARNING:** *Glass shards or other substances in the cushions are a common cause of tube breakage.*
- Do NOT touch a centrifuge while it is moving.

## Using Glassware

- **WARNING:** *Glass cools slowly. Do NOT touch glass that has been heated unless sufficient time has been allowed for cooling. Hold your hand over the glass to feel for heat emanating from it before touching. Always place hot glass on a hot pad, never on a metal or wooden desktop.*
- NEVER use glassware that is scratched or chipped—failure and breakage can result.
- Wrap or strip glassware with masking tape if it is to be used under vacuum or pressure. This will prevent flying pieces of glass in the event of an implosion or explosion.
- NEVER heat pipettes, volumetric flasks, or burettes—they can change volume as a result of expansion.
- Do NOT heat bottles, graduated cylinders, volumetric glassware, funnels, jars, droppers, watchglasses, desiccators, or glass plates.
- Manipulate heated glass with caution to avoid burns. Glass cools slowly.
- Heat and cool glass slowly, do NOT set a hot beaker on a cold or damp counter.
- Reduce scratches in glassware by using rubber-tipped stirring rods and coated clamps and by cleaning glassware immediately after use.
- When heating glassware, use a wire or ceramic screen to protect the glassware from the flame.
- NEVER eat or drink from laboratory glassware.
- Clean glassware thoroughly before returning it to storage.

## Working with Glass Tubing

- Always protect the hands with several layers of cloth when inserting glass tubing into or removing it from rubber stoppers.
- Lubricate glass tubing or thermometers with glycerin, water, or stopcock grease before insertion into a rubber stopper. Use a turning motion on the glass tubing when inserting it into a rubber stopper or rubber tubing.
- Remove glass tubing or thermometers from rubber stoppers as soon as possible to prevent the adherence of the rubber or cork to the glass. If the tubing or thermometer does stick to the stopper, only a teacher should attempt to separate the two. The teacher should wear gloves and goggles, and may be able to release the frozen area by running a stream of hot water over it. Using a strip of paper between ground joints, frequently lubricating stopcocks, or taking apart the equipment for storage will help limit the problem. It is advisable to cut the rubber stopper when a thermometer is involved to avoid breaking the thermometer.

- Commercially made glass tube cutters work well for cutting tubing. Wear safety goggles when cutting glass.
- After cutting glass tubing, always fire-polish the ends to remove any sharp edges. When bending glass tubing or fire polishing cut-glass tubing, NEVER hand the hot end of the tubing to anyone until it has cooled.

## Using Fume Hoods

- Work as far inside the hood as possible, at least 16 cm from the front edge.
- Work with the sash in the lowest position possible. NEVER work with the sash higher than chin level. The sash must be in a position to protect the head and upper body in case of an explosion. (See p. 137.)
- Close the sash when the hood exhaust system is not operating.
- Keep the interior light on so that the working area has proper illumination.
- Place blocks under large objects so that there is proper air flow under the objects.
- The sash must be kept in place except when setting up an activity. Do NOT conduct the activity until the sash has been replaced and is in the proper position.
- NEVER store chemicals or materials in the hood.
- NEVER place electrical apparatuses or items that may produce a spark in the fume hood.
- Even though the sash to the fume hood separates your face from the apparatus and materials under the hood, you also MUST use the personal safety equipment required for the activity.

## Using Electron Beams

- Cathode ray tubes, microwave tubes, and microwave tubes should be used with extreme care—operated at the lowest possible current and voltage with the operating time kept to a minium. It is recommended that these tubes be used only by the teacher for demonstrations and that the students stand at least 8 feet away from the tubes when they are in use. **WARNING:** *These tubes can produce X rays.* **WARNING:** *The glass in any vacuum tube becomes brittle with age and may implode.*
- Infrared/ultraviolet goggles or an approved welders' face shield should be worn when these light rays are used. **WARNING:** *Infrared radiation can damage the eye lens and cause cataracts. Ultraviolet rays can cause an inflammation of the conjunctiva of the eye and detachment of the retina.*
- Eye protection is required for protection from mercury light sources. **WARNING:** *Mercury light sources can emit ultraviolet rays.*
- Using direct sun as a light source in connection to lenses and prisms is NOT recommended. **WARNING:** *There is NO safe way to look directly at the sun.*

## Working with Biological Samples

- Consider using films, videos, and computer simulations in place of dissection activities.
- Carefully remove specimens from preservative solutions—wearing gloves and using tongs or forceps. **WARNING:** *Formalin solutions are carcinogenic. Any specimen held in a formalin solution should be soaked in a water bath in a fume hood and then thoroughly rinsed in running water for several minutes. Preferably, these specimens should be replaced with ones held in safer solutions (see pp. 124 and 129).*

- During dissection, do NOT hold the specimen in your hand. Cut down on the specimen, NOT up toward your body.
- When placing a blade onto a scalpel, leave the blade in the original package and hold the blade securely with the cutting edge away from your fingers. To remove the blade, use tweezers or forceps and always push the blade away from your body.
- Most insects can be anesthetized by freezing them in a jar for up to an hour. Ether or triethylamine are often used but are hazardous. **WARNING:** *Ether is flammable and may produce explosive peroxides. Triethylamine is safer than ether but is flammable, toxic if ingested, and corrosive to the skin and eyes.*
- Most insects may be killed by placing them in an airtight container in a freezer for 48 h. Ethyl acetate may be used in killing jars but is hazardous. **WARNING:** *Ethyl acetate is a fire hazard, explosion risk, an irritant to skin and eyes, and mildly toxic. Cyanide, carbon tetrachloride, and ether are too dangerous and are NOT recommended.*
- Closely monitor the use of syringes with needles by students. **WARNING:** *Puncture wounds are potential sources of hepatitis and embolisms. Always dispose of a syringe immediately after use; do NOT try to recap the needle.*

## International System of Units (SI)

Emphasize to students the need for using compatible units when carrying out investigations. Explain that not only should the units be converted to SI units, but also that all of the measurements used in an equation should be in the same units. For example, if some units of measurement in a relationship are in millimeters and some in centimeters, you must convert the amounts in centimeters to millimeters or the amounts in millimeters to centimeters. For further discussion, provide students with the SI Reference Sheet found on pp. 35–36.

## Assessing Students' Readiness for Lab Tasks

Before students begin work on assigned investigations, foster a climate of safety and proper equipment use by assessing the knowledge and proficiency of the skills required. This is especially important for students new to the science laboratory or who are new to your school. Survey the assessment worksheets provided on pp. 37–80 and select those that are pertinent to your course. The worksheets include laboratory task performance skills, measurement skills, analysis skills, and safety skills. The worksheets are listed on p. 29, and answers to the written worksheets appear on pp. 24–28.

For the Laboratory Tasks, you may wish to set up various stations in the classroom, having a small group of students demonstrate their skills in performing certain tasks, using the appropriate devices at each station. Rotate the groups through the stations until you have assessed the skills of each student. Rate each student's performance (see Glencoe's **Performance Assessment in the Science Classroom** booklet) and provide additional instruction to those students who need it.

# Answers to Student Worksheets

## Laboratory Equipment [pp. 30–34]

*Figure 1* **1.** Graduated cylinders **2.** Florence flask **3.** Beakers **4.** Crucible **5.** Petri dish **6.** Evaporating dish **7.** Erlenmeyer flask **8.** Long-stem funnel **9.** Watch glass

*Figure 2* **1.** Test tubes **2.** Test-tube rack **3.** Square-bottomed test tubes **4.** Rubber stoppers **5.** Corks **6.** Test-tube holder **7.** Test-tube brush

*Figure 3* **1.** Utility clamp **2.** Wire gauze **3.** Metal ring **4.** Laboratory burner **5.** Gas inlet **6.** Ring stand

*Figure 4* **1.** Stirring rod **2.** Funnel

*Figure 5* **1.** Thermometer **2.** Pipette **3.** Rubber tubing **4.** Pinch clamp **5.** Dropper **6.** Spatula **7.** Stirring rod **8.** Triangular file **9.** Forceps **10.** Scalpel

*Figure 6* **1.** Eyepiece **2.** Revolving nosepiece **3.** High-power objective lens **4.** Low-power objective lens **5.** Stage **6.** Diaphragm **7.** Adjustment knob **8.** Light

*Figure 7* **1.** Hickman still head **2.** Conical reaction vials **3.** Air reflux condenser **4.** Claisen head **5.** Hirsch funnel **6.** Filter flask **7.** Erlenmeyer flask (10 mL) **8.** Funnel **9.** Reaction tubes **10.** Magnetic stir bars **11.** Connector with support rod **12.** Pipette **13.** Stopper **14.** Spatula **15.** Centrifuge tube **16.** Glass tube connectors **17.** Syringe **18.** Flasks **19.** Tubing **20.** One-way stopcock **21.** Connectors **22.** Thermometer connectors

*Figure 8* **1.** Berol pipettes **2.** Blue litmus vial and litmus discs **3.** Microstand **4.** Plastic tubing (long and short) **5.** Zinc electrode **6.** Zinc coil **7.** Iron electrode **8.** Various tubes **9.** Microspatulas **10.** Dual well comboplate **11.** Microburner **12.** Syringe **13.** Chromatography paper strips **14.** pH color chart **15.** Gas collecting vial **16.** Microcaps **17.** Compass **18.** Microlids **19.** Current LED indicator

## Measurement Skills [pp. 61–68] *Accept close approximations.*

### Measuring Temperature
**1.** −2.5°    **2.** 37.95°    **3.** 8.2°    **4.** 86.5°    **5.** −10.4°    **6.** 34.5°

### Measuring Liquid Volume
**1.** 67.3 mL    **2.** 32.2 mL    **3.** 81.0 mL    **4.** 47.75 mL    **5.** 2.65 mL    **6.** 63.5 mL
**7.** 30.8 mL    **8.** 84.0 mL    **9.** 49.7 mL    **10.** 3.10 mL    **11.** 107.2 mL    **12.** 7.0 mL

### Finding Mass with a Balance
**1.** 47.52 g    **2.** 129.07 g    **3.** 6.86 g    **4.** 210.05 g

### Measuring Angles
**1.** 26°    **2.** 38°    **3.** 135°    **4.** D = 58°; E = 81°; F = 41°
**5.** G = 90°; H. = 121°; I = 75°; J = 74°

### Using a Metric Ruler
*Part 1.*
**A.** 12.50 cm    **B.** 11.30 cm    **C.** 13.25 cm    **D.** 13.95 cm    **E.** 10.30 cm    **F.** 12.00 cm
**G.** 9.70 cm    **H.** 12.96 cm    **I.** 14.35 cm

Part 2.

**Sample Data**

| Object | Length | Width | Height | Surface area/volume |
|--------|--------|-------|--------|---------------------|
| Index card | 12.8 cm | 7.6 cm | | $A = l \times w$<br>$A = 97.3 \text{ cm}^2$ |
| Microscopic slide | 7.5 cm | 2.5 cm | 0.080 cm | $V = l \times w \times h$<br>$V = 1.5 \text{ cm}^3$ |
| Petri dish | | diameter = 6.0 cm<br>radius = 3.0 cm | 1.5 cm | $V = \pi r^2 h$<br>$V = 42.4 \text{ cm}^3$ |
| Chalk | | diameter = 1.2 cm<br>radius = 0.60 cm | 8.5 cm | $V = \pi r^2 h$<br>$V = 9.6 \text{ cm}^3$ |
| Desktop | Answers will vary. | | | |
| | | | | |
| | | | | |

## Using a Metric Scale

| How far is it from the _____? | Metric measurement | | Actual distance (km) |
|------------------------------------|------|------|----------------------|
| | mm | cm | |
| Softball field to the lake | 130 | 13.0 | 1.3 |
| Meadow to the picnic area | 40 | 4.0 | 0.40 |
| Hickory grove to the lake | 57 | 5.7 | 0.57 |
| Pine forest to the picnic area | 69 | 6.9 | 0.69 |
| Softball field to the hickory grove | 93 | 9.3 | 0.93 |
| Softball field to the lake through the meadow | 64+72= 136 | 13.6 | 1.36 |

## Measuring with a Microscope

*Part 1.*

**A.** eyepiece      **B.** body tube      **C.** revolving nosepiece
**D.** low-power objective lens      **E.** high-power objective lens      **F.** stage
**G.** stage clips      **H.** base      **I.** mirror
**J.** diaphragm      **K.** arm      **L.** fine-adjustment knob
**M.** coarse-adjustment knob

*Part 2.*

**1.** arm; base      **2.** low-power      **3.** low-power      **4.** coarse      **5.** mirror      **6.** fine
**7.** lens paper

*Part 3.*

**1.** about 12 mm      **2.** 12,000 μ      **3.** 300 μ
**4a.** 200 μ      **4b.** 125 microns      **4c.** 150 μ

## Analysis Skills [pp. 69–75]

### Making a Table

| Number of Animal Species | |
|---|---|
| **Phylum** | **Number** |
| Arthropoda | 879,000 |
| Chordata | 44,000 |
| Cnidaria | 9,000 |
| Echinodermata | 6,000 |
| Mollusca | 50,000 |
| Porifera | 5,000 |
| Worm phyla | 41,000 |

### Making a Bar Graph

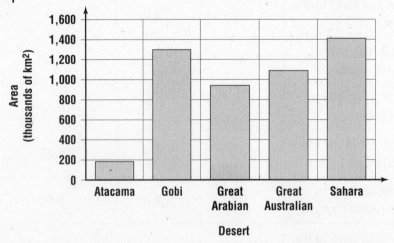

**Source:** *The New York Times 1999 Almanac*

26

## Making a Line Graph

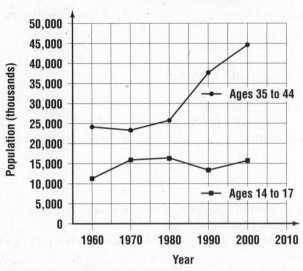

**U.S. Population by Age Group**

Population (thousands)

Ages 35 to 44

Ages 14 to 17

Year

**Source:** *The New York Times 1999 Almanac*

1. The 35-44 age group changed the most.
2. *Increased:* Between 1960 and 1970; between 1970 and 1980; and between 1990 and 2000. *Decreased:* Between 1980 and 1990.

## Making a Circle Graph

| Era | Number of years | Number of degrees |
|---|---|---|
| Cenozoic | 65,000,000 | 5 |
| Mesozoic | 160,000,000 | 13 |
| Paleozoic | 345,000,000 | 27 |
| Precambrian | 3,930,000,000 | 314 |

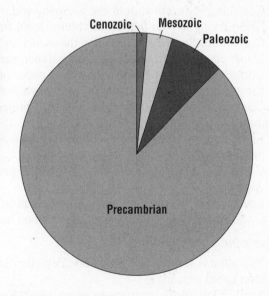

Cenozoic　Mesozoic　Paleozoic

Precambrian

## Using a Scientific Method

1. the mice on a normal protein diet
2. the protein in the food
3. the effect of different amounts of protein on growth in terms of mass
4. types or sources of different types of protein
5. the larger the number of individuals in a test, the more accurate the data and observations
6. Rework the hypothesis and test another variable.
7. problem, procedure, observation, conclusion

## Estimating Values

*Part 1.*

Sample data for actual values

1. **a.** 3.2 cm　　　　　　**b.** 1.8–2.1 m
   **c.** 3,600 km　　　　**d.** Answers will vary.

**2. a.** 0.5 g  **b.** 10 g  **c.** 2–5 kg  **d.** 0.5 kg
**3. a.** 0.25 L  **b.** 0.33 L  **c.** 5 mL  **d.** 0.20 L
**4. a.** 0°C  **b.** 37°C  **c.** 25°C  **d.** 30°–35°C
**5.** Answers will vary.  **6.** Answers will vary.  **7.** Answers will vary.

*Part 2.*

Sample data for actual values

**1. a.** 19 cm  **b.** 6 cm  **c.** 50–55 cm  **d.** 1,800 km
**2. a.** 1.5–2.0 g  **b.** 2 kg  **c.** 40–55 g  **d.** 15 kg
**3. a.** 0.33 L  **b.** 2 mL  **c.** 0.25 mL  **d.** 4 L
**4. a.** 100°C  **b.** 5°C  **c.** 55°C  **d.** 0°C or lower
**5.** Answers will vary.  **6.** Answers will vary.  **7.** Answers will vary.

## Safety Skills [pp. 76–80]

### Identifying Improper Safety Practices

1. Work in an uncluttered area; tie long hair back; wear safety goggles, gloves, and apron; do not point open end of test tube at anyone; be careful not to knock anything over.
2. Do not eat or drink anything in the laboratory; use fanning motion to detect odors; do not pull electrical plug by the cord; work in an uncluttered area.

### Correcting Unsafe Practices

1. Error: stirring with a thermometer
   Correction: Student should use a stirring rod.
2. Error: trying to read the liquid volume level from an angle
   Correction: Student should view the meniscus of the liquid at eye level.
3. Error: placing solid directly on the balance pan
   Correction: Student should use waxed paper or a container.
4. Error: pushing straight down on tubing while holding it near the top
   Correction: Student should use towels to protect hands, hold glass near stopper, and use twisting motion
5. Error: carrying microscope incorrectly; Base and stage could fall down; mirror might fall out; not protecting eyes.
   Correction: Student should use one hand to grasp the arm and use other hand under the base; wear goggles.
6. Error: Handling a live animal with bare hands; not protecting eyes.
   Correction: Student should use gloves when handling a live animal to avoid being bitten.

### Developing Safety Policies

1. Everyone is responsible for safety. Pay attention to what you're doing. Be considerate of others. Don't fool around.
2. Lack of knowledge may cause an accident. Read through procedures carefully.
3. Perform activities only when a teacher is present and do only those activities authorized by a teacher.
4. Always protect clothing and eyes in the laboratory by wearing aprons and goggles.

### Using Safety Devices Correctly

1. fire blanket: When hair or clothing is on fire, apply blanket from head down to prevent fanning flames upward.
2. $CO_2$ fire extinguisher: Use on all fires except those involving people. Frostbite can result from skin contact with solid carbon dioxide.
3. goggles: wear at all times when doing lab work.
4. eyewash station: Wash face, eyelids, and eyes for at least 15 min. Hold the eyelids open, rotating the eyes so that water can flow on all surfaces.
5. safety hood or vent: Any procedures involving poisonous or irritating fumes should be done under a safety hood.

## Blackline Masters Divider

# *Laboratory Equipment*

**Figure 1**

1. _____     2. _____

3. _____

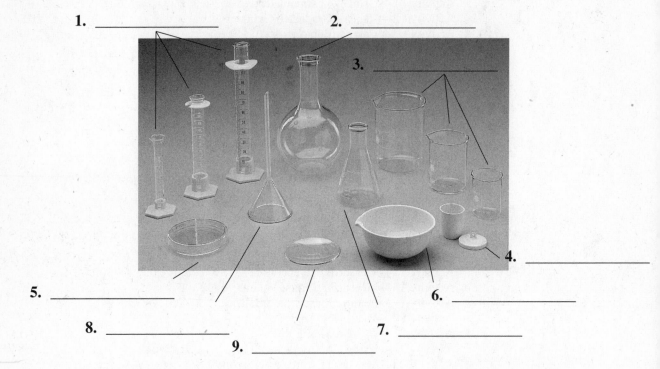

4. _____

5. _____

8. _____

9. _____

7. _____

6. _____

**Figure 2**

1. _____

3. _____     2. _____

4. _____

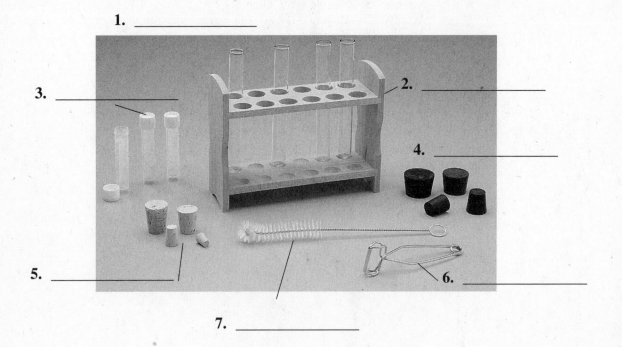

5. _____     6. _____

7. _____

# *Laboratory Equipment (continued)*

**Figure 3**

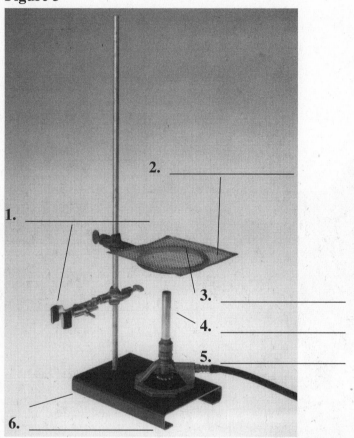

1. _____
2. _____
3. _____
4. _____
5. _____
6. _____

**Figure 4**

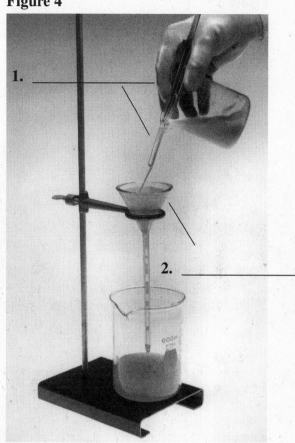

1. _____
2. _____

**Figure 5**

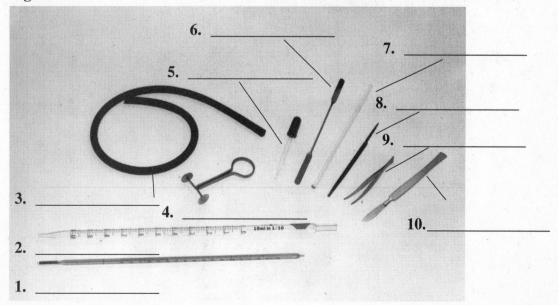

1. _____
2. _____
3. _____
4. _____
5. _____
6. _____
7. _____
8. _____
9. _____
10. _____

# Laboratory Equipment (continued)

**Figure 6**

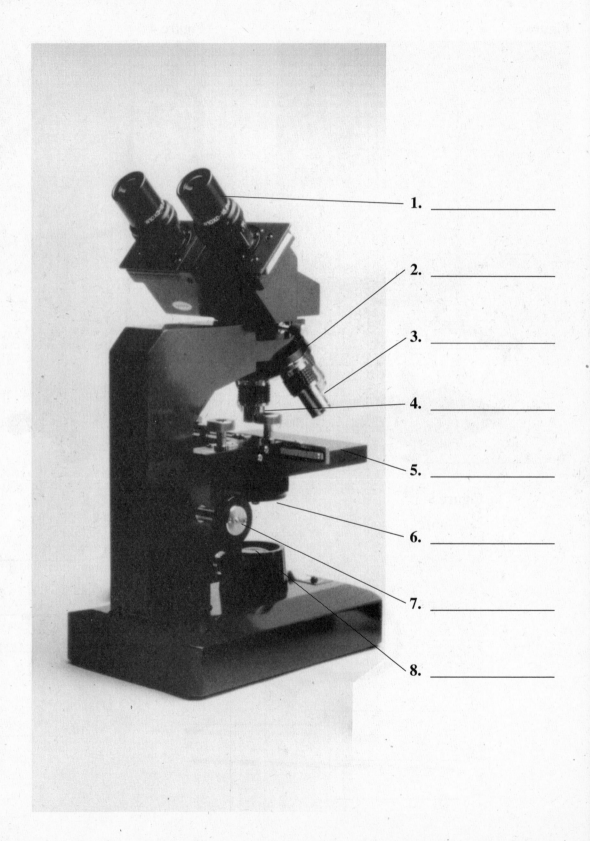

1. _____

2. _____

3. _____

4. _____

5. _____

6. _____

7. _____

8. _____

# *Laboratory Equipment (continued)*

**Figure 7**

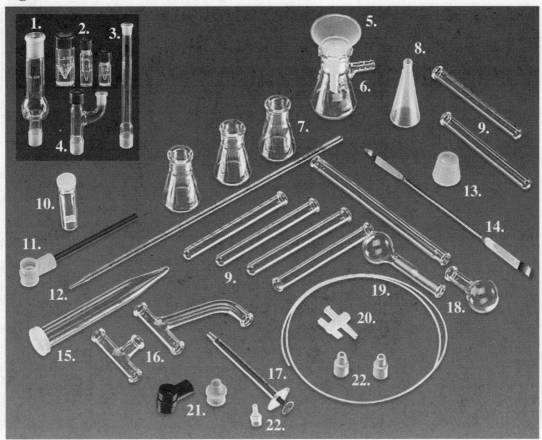

1. _____
2. _____
3. _____
4. _____
5. _____
6. _____
7. _____
8. _____
9. _____
10. _____
11. _____

12. _____
13. _____
14. _____
15. _____
16. _____
17. _____
18. _____
19. _____
20. _____
21. _____
22. _____

# Laboratory Equipment (continued)

**Figure 8**

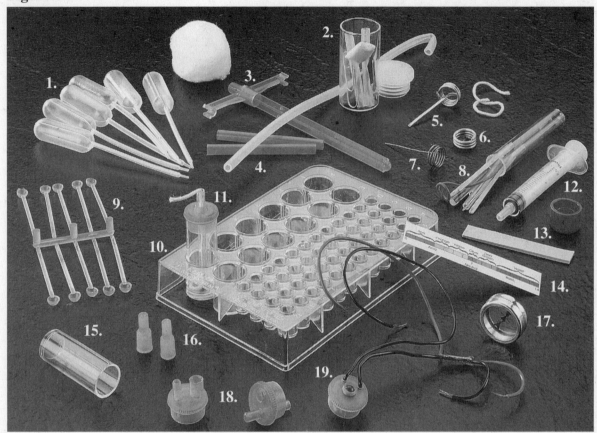

1. _____
2. _____
3. _____
4. _____
5. _____
6. _____
7. _____
8. _____
9. _____
10. _____

11. _____
12. _____
13. _____
14. _____
15. _____
16. _____
17. _____
18. _____
19. _____

# SI Reference Sheet

The International System of Units (SI) is accepted as the standard for measurement throughout most of the world. Frequently used SI units are listed in **Table 1** and some supplementary SI units in **Table 2.**

**Table 1**

| Frequently Used SI Units | |
|---|---|
| Length | 1 millimeter (mm) = 100 micrometers (μm)<br>1 centimeter (cm) = 10 millimeters (mm)<br>1 meter (m) = 100 centimeters (cm)<br>1 kilometer (km) = 1,000 meters (m)<br>1 light-year = 9,460,000,000,000 kilometers (km) |
| Area | 1 square meter ($m^2$) = 10,000 square centimeters ($cm^2$)<br>1 square kilometer ($km^2$) = 1,000,000 square meters ($m^2$) |
| Volume | 1 milliliter (mL) = 1 cubic centimeter ($cm^3$)<br>1 liter (L) = 1,000 milliliters (mL) |
| Mass | 1 gram (g) = 1,000 milligrams (mg)<br>1 kilogram (kg) = 1,000 grams (g)<br>1 metric ton = 1,000 kilograms (kg) |
| Time | 1 s = 1 second |

**Table 2**

| Supplementary SI Units | | | |
|---|---|---|---|
| **Measurement** | **Unit** | **Symbol** | **Expressed in base units** |
| Energy | joule | J | $kg \cdot m^2/s^2$ |
| Force | newton | N | $kg \cdot m/s^2$ |
| Power | watt | W | $kg \cdot m^2/s^3$ or J/s |
| Pressure | pascal | Pa | $kg/m \cdot s^2$ or $N \cdot m$ |

Sometimes quantities are measured using different SI units. In order to use them together in an equation, you must convert all of the quantities into the same unit. To convert, you multiply by a conversion factor. A conversion factor is a ratio that is equal to one. Make a conversion factor by building a ratio of equivalent units. Place the new units in the numerator and the old units in the denominator. For example, to convert 1.255 L to mL, multiply 1.255 L by the appropriate ratio as follows:

$$1.255 \text{ L} \times 1,000 \text{ mL}/1 \text{ L} = 1,255 \text{ mL}$$

The unit L cancels just as if it were a number.

Temperature measurements in SI often are made in degrees Celsius. Celsius temperature is a supplementary unit derived from the base unit kelvin. The Celsius scale (°C) has 100 equal graduations between the freezing temperature (0°C) and the boiling temperature of water (100°C). The following relationship exists between the Celsius and kelvin temperature scales:

$$K = °C + 273$$

# SI Reference Sheet (continued)

To convert from °F to °C, you can:

1. For exact amounts, use the equation at the bottom of **Table 3**, or
2. For approximate amounts, find °F on the thermometer at the left of **Figure 1** and determine °C on the thermometer at the right.

**Table 3**

| SI Metric to English Conversions | | | |
|---|---|---|---|
| | **When you have:** | **Multiply by:** | **To find:** |
| **Length** | inches | 2.54 | centimeters |
| | centimeters | 0.39 | inches |
| | feet | 0.30 | meters |
| | meters | 3.28 | feet |
| | yards | 0.91 | meters |
| | meters | 1.09 | yards |
| | miles | 1.61 | kilometers |
| | kilometers | 0.62 | miles |
| **Mass and weight*** | ounces | 28.35 | grams |
| | grams | 0.04 | ounces |
| | pounds | 0.45 | kilograms |
| | kilograms | 2.20 | pounds |
| | tons | 0.91 | metric tons |
| | metric tons | 1.10 | tons |
| | pounds | 4.45 | newtons |
| | newtons | 0.23 | pounds |
| **Volume** | cubic inches | 16.39 | cubic centimeters |
| | milliliters | 0.06 | cubic inches |
| | cubic feet | 0.03 | cubic meters |
| | cubic meters | 35.31 | cubic feet |
| | liters | 1.06 | quarts |
| | liters | 0.26 | gallons |
| | gallons | 3.78 | liters |
| **Area** | square inches | 6.45 | square centimeters |
| | square centimeters | 0.16 | square inches |
| | square feet | 0.09 | square meters |
| | square meters | 10.76 | square feet |
| | square miles | 2.59 | square kilometers |
| | square kilometers | 0.39 | square miles |
| | hectares | 2.47 | acres |
| | acres | 0.40 | hectares |
| **Temperature** | Fahrenheit | $\frac{5}{9}(°F - 32)$ | Celsius |
| | Celsius | $\frac{9}{5}°C + 32$ | Fahrenheit |

\* Weight as measured in standard Earth gravity

**Figure 1**

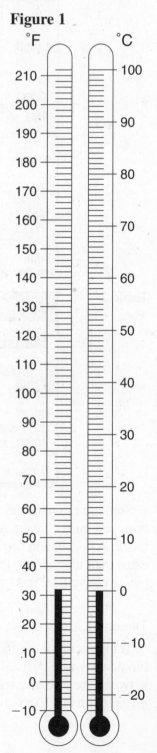

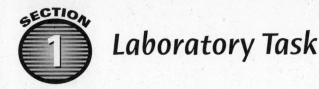

# Laboratory Task

## Using a Thermometer

### What You'll Do

You will accurately determine the temperature of the water, positioning the thermometer correctly.

### Materials

- thermometer
- beaker (or other container)
- hot water

### Safety Precautions

**WARNING:** *Notify your teacher immediately if you break the thermometer.*

**WARNING:** *Be sure to use a thermometer that is calibrated for high temperatures when measuring the temperature of hot or boiling liquids.*

**WARNING:** *NEVER "shake down" a thermometer to reset it.*

**WARNING:** *NEVER stir anything with a thermometer.*

### Procedure

1. Place the bulb of the thermometer in the center of the hot water in the beaker. Do NOT allow the bulb to touch the bottom or sides of the beaker (or other container). See **Figure 1**.
2. Watch the column in the thermometer until it stops moving.
3. Read the thermometer while it is still in the water. (Once the thermometer is removed from the liquid, the column of mercury or alcohol will soon adjust to the temperature of the air.)

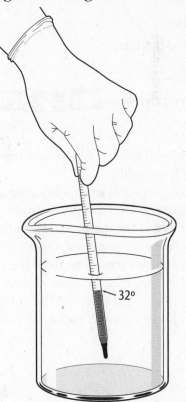

**Figure 1: Using a thermometer**

---

### Task Assessment

_____ I positioned the thermometer correctly and read the thermometer accurately.

_____ I need to try the task again because _____

_____

_____.

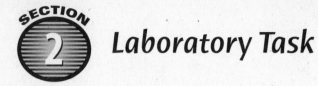

# Laboratory Task

## Using a Graduated Cylinder

When you measure the volume of a liquid in a glass cylinder, the view of the surface of the liquid is always curved. This curved surface is called the *meniscus*. Most of the liquids you will be measuring will have a concave meniscus.

**Note:** Liquid in many plastic cylinders does not form a meniscus. If you are using a plastic graduated cylinder and no meniscus is noticeable, read the volume from the level of the liquid.

### What You'll Do

Determine the volume of water in a graduated cylinder.

### Materials

- graduated cylinder
- colored water

### Safety Precautions

### Procedure

1. Pour colored water into a graduated cylinder, but do not fill it to the top.
2. View the meniscus from a horizontal line of sight. See **Figure 1**. Do NOT try to make a reading looking up or down at the meniscus. Hold the apparatus up so that its sides are at a right angle to your eye.
3. Read a concave meniscus from the bottom. (This measurement gives the most precise volume, because the liquid tends to creep up the sides of a glass container.) Read a convex meniscus from the top.

**Figure 1: Reading liquid volume**

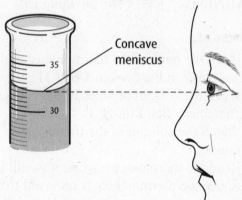

### Task Assessment

_____     I determined the volume of water in a graduated cylinder correctly.

_____     I need to try the task again because _____

_____

_____

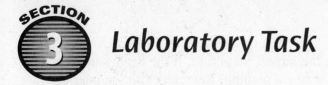

# Laboratory Task

## Using a Balance

The balance you use may look somewhat different from the ones in **Figure 1**; however, all beam balances have some common features. The following technique should be used in transporting a balance, if you are instructed to do so by your teacher.

- Be sure all riders are back to the zero point
- If the balance has a lock mechanism to lock the pan(s), be sure it is on.
- Place one hand under the balance and the other hand on the beam's support.

**Figure 1: Pan or beam balances**

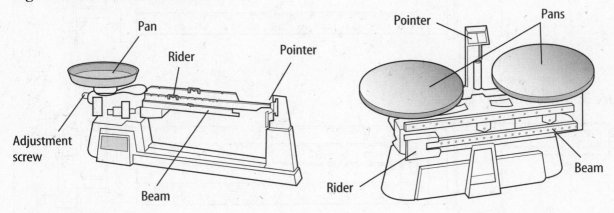

## What You'll Do

1. Properly carry the balance to your work area, then back to its original location.
2. Determine the mass of the rubber stopper accurately.

## Materials

- balance
- rubber stopper

## Safety Precautions

## Procedure

1. Slide all riders back to the zero point. Check to see that the pointer swings freely along the scale. You do not have to wait for the pointer to stop at the zero point. The beam should swing an equal distance above and below the zero point. Use the adjustment screw to obtain an equal swing of the beams, if necessary. You must repeat this procedure to "zero" the balance every time you use it.
2. Place the object to be massed on waxed paper on the pan. **WARNING:** *NEVER put a hot object directly on the balance pan.* Mass the container first so that you can subtract that from the total mass (see Step 3) to get the mass of the object. **WARNING:** *NEVER pour chemicals directly on the balance pan.*

_Activity 3, continued from p. 39_

3. Move the riders along the beams beginning with the largest mass first. If the beams are notched, make sure that all riders are in a notch before you take a reading. Remember, the pointer does not have to stop swinging, but the swing should be an equal distance above and below the zero point on the scale.
4. Add the masses indicated on the beams to get the mass of the object. For example, the beams in **Figure 2** show that the mass of an object is 47.52 g. The beams in **Figure 3** show that the mass of another object is 100.39 g.

**Figure 2: Mass is 47.52 g.**

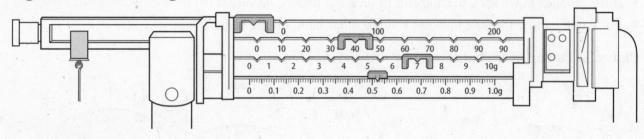

**Figure 3: Mass is 100.39 g.**

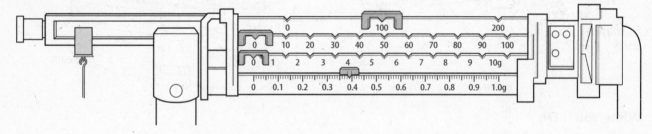

## Task Assessment

_____ I carried and used the balance correctly.

_____ I massed the rubber stopper accurately.

_____ I need to try the task(s) again because _____

_____

_____

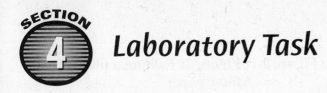

# Laboratory Task

## Decanting and Filtering a Liquid

**Filtration** is a common process of separation used in most laboratories. The liquid is **decanted**, that is, the liquid is separated from the solid by carefully pouring off the liquid, leaving only the solid material.

### What You'll Do

1. Correctly set up the equipment for a filtration procedure.
2. Decant a liquid from the residue (sand).

### Materials

- beakers (2)
- water
- sand
- stirring rod
- filter paper
- funnel
- ring stand
- triangle pipe stem

### Safety Precautions

### Procedure

1. Pour the water and sand into one beaker.
2. Decant the water into the other beaker. **WARNING:** *To avoid splashing and to maintain control, pour the liquid down a stirring rod.* See **Figure 1**.

**Figure 1: Decanting liquid from a solid**

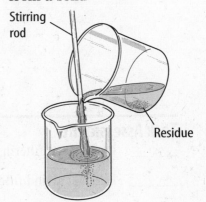

Stirring rod

Residue

*Activity 4, continued*

**3.** Prepare the filter paper for the filtration step. See **Figure 2**.

**Figure 2: Folding a piece of filter paper**

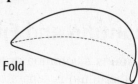

Fold

Fold again

Tear off outer corner as shown

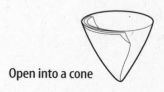

Open into a cone

**4.** Pour the water through filter paper to catch any sand that has not settled to the bottom of the beaker. See **Figure 3**.

**Figure 3: Filtering**

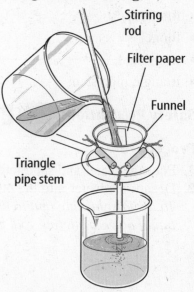

Stirring rod

Filter paper

Funnel

Triangle pipe stem

---

## Task Assessment

_____ I set up the filtering equipment correctly.

_____ I decanted and filtered a liquid from the residue (sand).

_____ I need to try the task(s) again because _____

_____

_____

_____

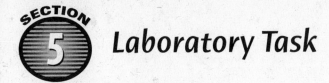

# Laboratory Task

## Smelling a Substance

### What You'll Do
Use the correct method to smell a substance. **WARNING:** *Tell your teacher immediately if you are sensitive or allergic to certain odors (vapors).*

### Materials
- test tube
- substance (nontoxic) provided by your teacher

### Safety Precautions
**WARNING:** *NEVER touch, taste, or smell any substance in the laboratory unless instructed to do so by your teacher.*

### Procedure
1. Hold the test tube away form your face. Do NOT bring the container to your nose. **WARNING:** *NEVER smell a substance directly. It may be too concentrated and can cause injury.*
2. Use a fanning motion to direct the vapor toward you. See **Figure 1**.

**Figure 1: Smelling a substance**

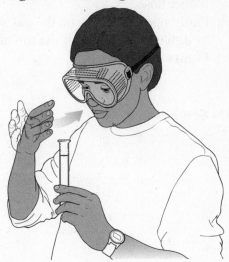

### Task Assessment
_____ I used the correct method to smell a substance.

_____ I need to try the task again because _____

_____

_____.

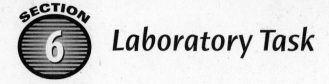

# Laboratory Task

## Lighting a Gas Burner

Most laboratory gas burners are constructed similarly, regardless of the type of gas.

### What You'll Do
Correctly set up and light a burner and adjust the flame.

### Materials
- laboratory gas burner
- rubber hose
- striker or lighter

### Safety Precautions

### Procedure
1. Connect the hose of the burner to a gas supply with a rubber hose.
2. Partly open the valve on the gas supply, and hold a striker or lighter to the edge of the top of the burner. See **Figure 1**.

**Figure 1: Lighting a burner**

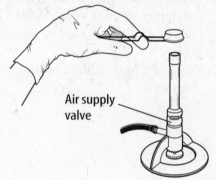

Air supply valve

*Activity 6, continued*

3. Change the size of the flame by opening and closing the gas supply valve on the bottom of the burner. See **Figure 2**.
4. If the flame is yellow, turn the air supply valve on the burner tube to increase the amount of air.
5. If the flame goes out, reduce the air supply by turning the burner tube in the opposite direction.

**Figure 2: Adjusting gas and air supplies**

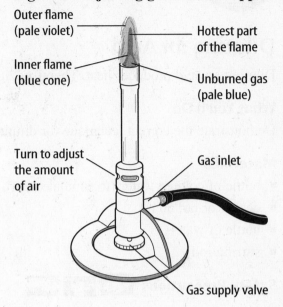

Outer flame (pale violet)

Hottest part of the flame

Inner flame (blue cone)

Unburned gas (pale blue)

Turn to adjust the amount of air

Gas inlet

Gas supply valve

## Task Assessment

_____    I correctly connected the rubber hose to the burner.

_____    I adjusted the gas and air supplies to get a blue flame.

_____    I need to try the task(s) again because _____

_____

_____ .

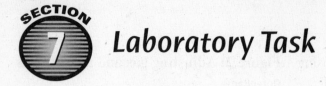

# Laboratory Task

## Diluting an Acid

Diluting an acid produces heat. Therefore, it is important to do so correctly.

### What You'll Do

Demonstrate the correct technique for diluting an acid.

### Materials

- bottle of colored water (to simulate acid), 15 mL
- beaker or jar, 50 mL
- bottle of water
- stirring rod

### Safety Precautions

### Procedure

1. Pour the plain water into the beaker to a level of 20 mL.
   **WARNING:** *ALWAYS add the acid to water. NEVER add water to the acid.*
2. Pour the acid (colored water) SLOWLY down the stirring rod into the beaker and continually stir the solution. See **Figure 1**.
3. Add plain water as needed to fill the beaker to 45 mL.

**Figure 1: Diluting an acid**

---

## Task Assessment

_____    I demonstrated the correct technique for diluting an acid.

_____    I need to try the task again because _____

_____

_____ .

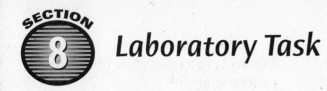

# Laboratory Task

## Inserting Glass Tubing into a Rubber Stopper

This procedure also is used for inserting thermometers in rubber stoppers.

### What You'll Do

Insert glass tubing into a stopper correctly.

### Materials

- glass tubing
- glycerol or soap water
- one-hole rubber stopper
- cloth towel

### Safety Precautions

**WARNING:** *This procedure can be dangerous if you are not careful.*

**WARNING:** Mercury thermometers are NOT recommended. Notify your teacher immediately if any thermometer breaks.

### Procedure

1. Check the size of the holes in the rubber stopper to be sure they are just slightly smaller than the glass tubing. (The rubber stopper should stretch enough to hold the glass tubing firmly.)
2. Place a drop of glycerol or some water on the end of the glass tubing. (Glycerol acts as a lubricant to help make the tubing go through the stopper more easily. See **Figure 1**.
3. Wrap the glass tubing and the stopper in a towel. **WARNING:** *NEVER skip this step.*

**Figure 1: Lubricating glass tubing**

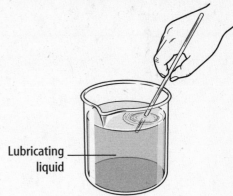

Lubricating liquid

*Activity 8, continued*

4. Push the tubing through the stopper using a gentle force and a twisting motion. Your hands should not be more than 1 cm apart. See **Figure 2**. **WARNING:** *Never hold the tubing or stopper in such a way that the end of the tubing is pointed toward or pushing against the palm of your hand. If the tubing breaks, you can injure your hand if it is held this way.*

**Figure 2: Inserting glass tubing into a rubber stopper**

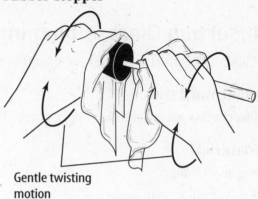

Gentle twisting motion

5. Continue Step 4 until the end of the glass tubing protrudes from the stopper. See **Figure 3**.

**Figure 3: Finished Product**

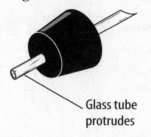

Glass tube protrudes

## Task Assessment

_____    I inserted glass tubing into the rubber stopper correctly.

_____    I need to try the task again because _____

_____

_____.

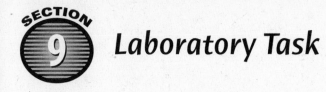

## Laboratory Task

# Heating a Substance in a Test Tube

## What You'll Do

Heat water in a test tube correctly.

## Materials

- gas burner or electric hot plate
- test tube (square-bottomed for use with the hot plate)
- test-tube holder
- striker or sparker
- water
- thermal mitts

## Safety Precautions

## Procedure

1. Light the gas burner (refer to Laboratory Task on Lighting a Gas Burner) or turn on the hot plate. **WARNING:** *The hot plate may be hot already. Handle with care.*
2. Hold the test tube with the test-tube holder.
3. Partially fill the test tube with water.
4. With a gas burner, hold the filled test tube over the flame, moving the tube constantly for even heating. See **Figure 1**. With the hot plate, hold the test tube flat on the hot plate. (Do NOT boil the water.) **WARNING:** *Always point the mouth of the heated test tube away from yourself and others.*

**Figure 1: Heating a test tube using a gas burner**

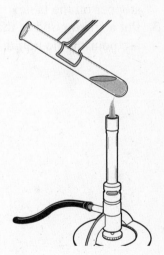

## Task Assessment

_____     I heated water in a test tube correctly.

_____     I need to try the task again because _____

_____

_____

# SECTION 10 *Laboratory Task*

## Transferring Liquids

### What You'll Do

Transfer a liquid from one container to another correctly.

### Materials

- reagent bottle with 50 mL colored water (to simulate acid)
- 100-mL beaker
- stirring rod

### Safety Precautions

**WARNING:** *NEVER touch chemicals with your hands or let them touch your face or body.*

**WARNING:** *Notify your teacher immediately if a chemical is spilled.*

### Procedure

1. Remove the stopper as shown in **Figure 1**.
2. Hold the stopper as shown in **Figure 1**. Do NOT put the stopper on the table.
3. Put a stirring rod in the second container into which you are pouring the liquid.

**Figure 1: Removing a stopper from a reagent bottle**

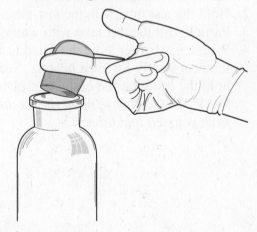

*Activity 10, continued*

4. Hold the stirring rod against the lip of the first container as shown in **Figure 2**.

5. Pour the liquid from the first container slowly down the stirring rod into the second container. **WARNING:** *If any liquid runs down the outside of the first container, rinse it with water before returning it to the shelf. (If the container is not rinsed, it may damage the shelf.)* **WARNING:** *If the liquid is an acid, wipe spills with a paper towel, do NOT pour water on the acid.*

6. Replace the stopper in the first container when you are finished.

**Figure 2: Pouring a liquid, holding the stopper to the reagent bottle**

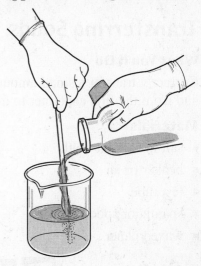

## Task Assessment

_____    I transferred a liquid from one container to another correctly.

_____    I need to try the task(s) again because _____

_____

_____.

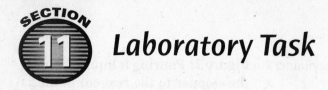

# Laboratory Task

## Transferring Solids

### What You'll Do

Correctly transfer a small amount of a solid chemical from one container to a wide-mouth container and from the first container to a test tube.

### Materials

- salt in reagent bottle
- beaker or jar
- test tube
- spatula or spoon
- waxed paper

### Safety Precautions

**WARNING:** *NEVER touch chemicals with your hands or let them touch your face or body.*

### Procedure

1. Use a clean spoon or spatula to remove the solid material from its container as shown in **Figure 1**. Or, rotate the bottle back and forth to shake out the solid.

**Figure 1: Removing a solid from a container**

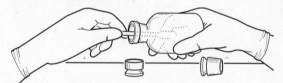

2. Place the solid material on a piece of creased, waxed paper and add the solid very carefully to your container. (See **Figure 2**.)

**Figure 2: Transferring a solid to a wide-mouth container**

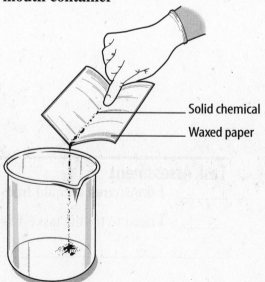

Solid chemical

Waxed paper

*Activity 11, continued*

3. Transfer the solid to a test tube by folding the paper as shown in **Figure 3**.
4. If the solid is to be massed, remember to use waxed paper or a container. Do NOT place the solid directly on the balance pan.

**Figure 3: Removing a solid from a container**

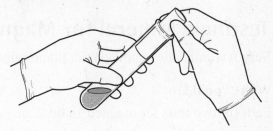

## Task Assessment

_____ I correctly transferred a solid to a wide-mouth container and to a test tube.

_____ I need to try the task again because _____

_____

_____.

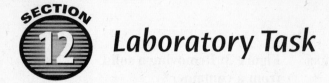

# Laboratory Task

## Testing a Mineral for Magnetism

Very few minerals are magnetic. Some minerals become magnetic only if they are heated.

### What You'll Do

Perform two tests for magnetism on a mineral.

### Materials

- mineral
- hammer
- magnet
- burner
- tongs
- thermal mitts

### Safety Precautions

### Procedure

**Test 1:**

1. Break the mineral into small pieces.
2. Hold the magnet toward the pieces to see whether the magnet attracts them. See **Figure 1**.

**Test 2:**

1. Hold a small piece of the mineral in a flame with tongs. **WARNING:** *Be sure to wear goggles and use a thermal mitt.*
2. Hold the magnet toward the heated pieces to see whether the magnet attracts them.

**Figure 1: Testing for magnetism**

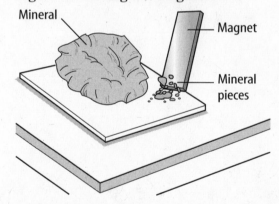

---

### Task Assessment

_____ I performed two tests for magnetism correctly.

_____ I need to try the task again because _____

_____

_____.

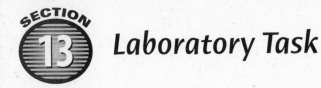

# Laboratory Task

## Testing a Mineral for Streak

**Streak** is the color of the powdered mineral that is left when the mineral is drawn across a nonglazed, porcelain plate called a **streak plate**. Streak is used to help identify an unknown mineral.

### What You'll Do
Test a mineral for streak to identify the mineral.

### Materials
- mineral
- streak plate
- list that matches streak colors to minerals

### Safety Precautions

### Procedure
1. Scratch a streak plate with a mineral. See **Figure 1**.
2. Match the color of the streak to a list of streak colors of known minerals.

**Figure 1: Testing for streak**

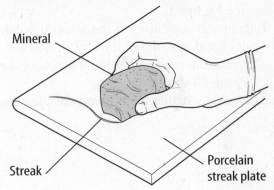

Mineral

Streak

Porcelain streak plate

---

### Task Assessment

_____ I performed the streak test correctly.

_____ I need to try the task again because _____

_____

_____.

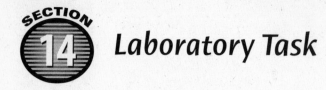

# Laboratory Task

## Testing a Mineral for Cleavage and Fracture

A mineral has **cleavage** if it breaks under stress to form smooth, flat, reflective faces. A mineral that does not cleave is said to **fracture** or break along irregular surfaces.

### What You'll Do

Strike a chunk of mineral properly to see whether it has cleavage or fracture.

### Materials

- mineral chunk
- hammer
- chisel

### Safety Precautions

### Procedure

1. Place the chisel in the center of the mineral chunk. **See Figure 1.**
2. Hammer the chisel. If the mineral breaks or does not break parallel to the chisel, turn the mineral and repeat the process until you have checked for cleavage in all directions.
3. Decide whether the mineral has cleavage or fracture.

**Figure 1: Testing for mineral cleavage**

---

### Task Assessment

_____ I tested the mineral for cleavage and fracture properly.

_____ I need to try the task again because _____

_____

_____ .

---

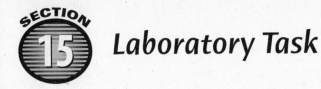

# Laboratory Task

## Testing a Mineral for Hardness

**Hardness** is the resistance of a mineral to being scratched. When testing for hardness, one mineral is harder than another if the first mineral can scratch the second mineral.

### What You'll Do

Perform a test to determine whether a mineral is harder or softer than a known mineral.

### Materials

- set of Mohs' minerals
- mineral (known hardness)
- mineral (unknown hardness)

### Safety Precautions

### Procedure

1. Scratch a mineral of unknown hardness against a mineral with a known hardness. See **Figure 1**.
2. Reverse the minerals and scratch again to confirm your results. If the minerals are nearly the same hardness, a scratch may be difficult to see.
3. Use a set of Mohs' minerals to determine the hardness of unknown minerals. If Mohs' minerals are not available, you may substitute common objects. If a mineral can be scratched by a fingernail, it has a hardness of about 2; a copper penny, a hardness of 3; a nail, a hardness of 5 to 6; a knife blade, a hardness of 6; and a piece of glass, a hardness of 6 to 7.

**Figure 1: Testing for hardness**

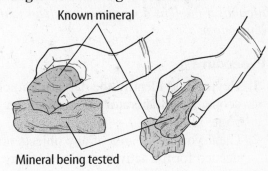

Known mineral

Mineral being tested

### Task Assessment

_____ I tested an unknown mineral for hardness correctly.

_____ I need to try the task again because _____

_____

_____.

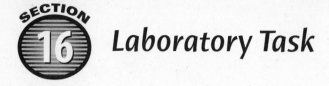

# Laboratory Task

## Using a Microscope

### What You'll Do

1. Correctly carry the microscope from its storage place to your work area and back to its storage place.
2. Place a prepared slide on the stage and bring it into sharp focus.

### Materials

- microscope
- prepared slide

### Safety Precautions

**WARNING:** *Do NOT touch the lenses. Use only special lens paper to clean the lenses. Moisten the lens paper with a drop of water or alcohol if the lens does not wipe clean with dry lens paper.*

### Procedure

1. Review and identify the parts of a microscope. (See Laboratory Equipment on page 32.)
2. Clear your work area of any objects not needed for the activity you're working on.
3. Pick up the microscope from its storage area. ALWAYS carry the microscope with both hands. Hold the arm with one hand. Put your other hand under the base as shown in **Figure 1** on the next page.
4. Place the microscope on a table gently, with the arm facing you.
5. Plug in the cord to the microscope. **WARNING:** *Make sure that electric cords from microscopes or lamps do NOT block aisles.*
6. Turn on the light if the microscope has one. (If the microscope does not have a light, use a lamp as a light source. **WARNING:** (*Outdoors, NEVER use direct sunlight as a light source. It can damage your eyes.*)

7. Look through the eyepiece and adjust the mirror so that light from the lamp is reflected up through the opening in the stage.
8. Place the slide in the stage slips. **WARNING:** *Be careful when using coverslips and microscope slides because they may crack or shatter when dropped.*
9. Adjust the diaphragm so that the greatest amount of light comes through the opening. (The circle of light that you see is called the *field of view*.)
10. Turn the nosepiece so that the low power objective lens (10X) clicks into place.
11. Focus the low power objective lens by turning the coarse adjustment knob. **WARNING:** *When using the coarse adjustment to lower the low power objective, always look at the microscope from the side. If you look through the eyepiece, you may accidentally force the objective into the coverslip.*

*Activity 16, continued*

## Figure 1: Carrying a microscope properly

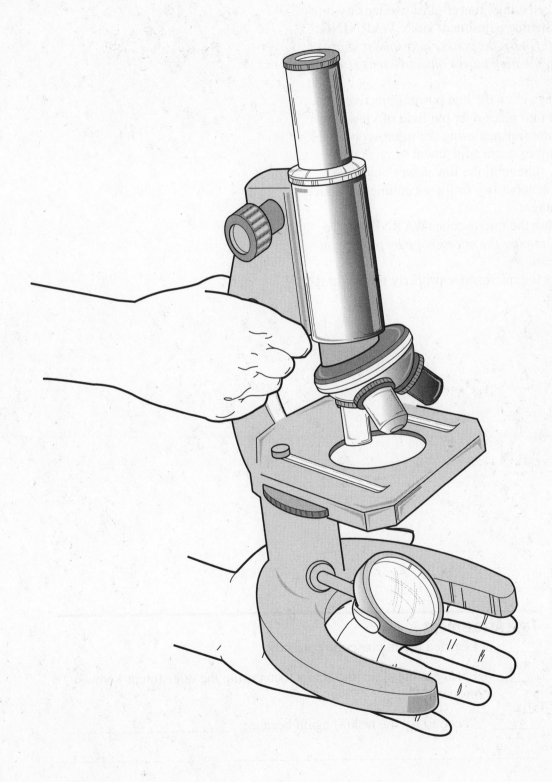

*Activity 16, continued*

12. Turn the nosepiece again until the high power objective lens clicks into place.

13. Focus the high power objective lens by turning the fine adjustment knob. **WARNING:** *NEVER turn the coarse adjustment knob when the high power objective lens is in place.*

14. Always click the low power objective lens back into place over the field of view when you are finished using the microscope.

15. Turn the coarse adjustment to raise the body tube until the low power objective lens is about two or three centimeters above the stage.

16. Unplug the microscope. **WARNING:** *Do NOT unplug the microscope by pulling on the cord.*

17. Carry the microscope properly to its storage place.

## Task Assessment

_____ I carried the microscope correctly.

_____ I brought the slide into sharp focus using the adjustment knobs properly.

_____ I need to try the task(s) again because _____

_____

_____ .

# Measurement Skill

## Measuring Temperature

Read the temperature on each of the thermometers below.

1. _____

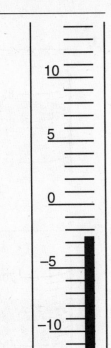

2. _____

3. _____

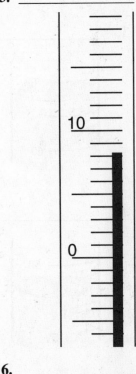

4. _____

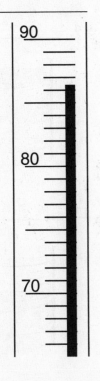

5. _____

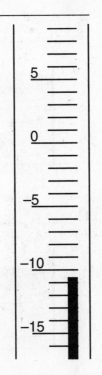

6. _____

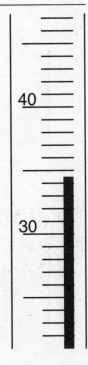

# SECTION 18 Measurement Skill

## Measuring Liquid Volume

Not all graduated cylinders have the same scale.

*Read the volume of liquid in each of the graduated cylinders below.*

1. _____

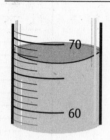

2. _____

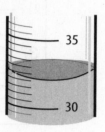

3. _____

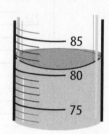

4. _____

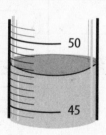

5. _____

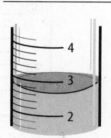

6. _____

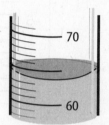

7. _____

8. _____

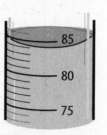

9. _____

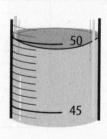

10. _____

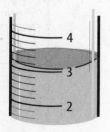

11. _____

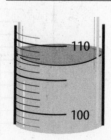

12. _____

# SECTION 19 Measurement Skill

## Finding Mass with a Balance

*Determine the mass shown on each of the balances.*

**1.** The mass of the object would be read as _____.

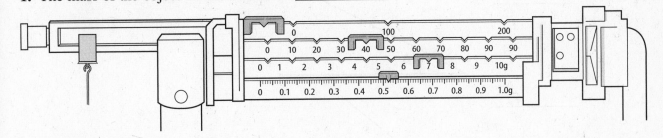

**2.** The mass of the object would be read as _____.

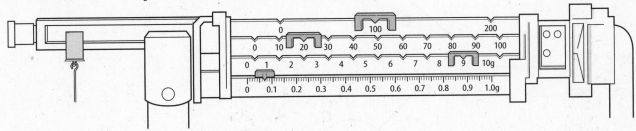

**3.** The mass of the object would be read as _____.

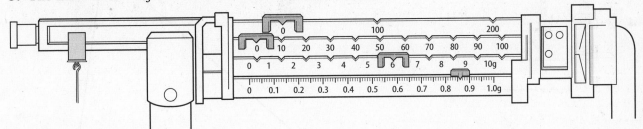

**4.** The mass of the object would be read as _____.

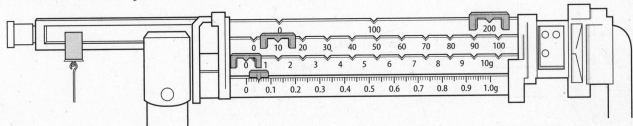

# Measurement Skill

## Measuring Angles

*Using your protractor, measure the size of the angles below.*

**1.** ∠ A = _____

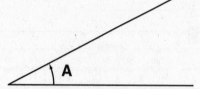

**2.** ∠ B = _____

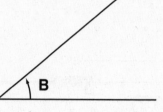

**3.** ∠ C = _____

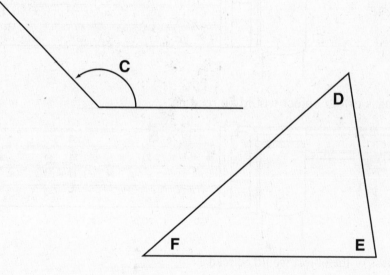

**4.** ∠ D = _____

∠ E = _____

∠ F = _____

**5.** ∠ G = _____

∠ H = _____

∠ I = _____

∠ J = _____

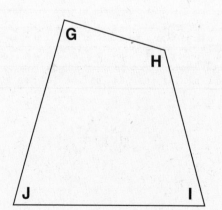

# SECTION 21  Measurement Skill

## Using a Metric Ruler

*Write the length that corresponds to each arrow along the ruler.*

A. _____  B. _____  C. _____

D. _____  E. _____  F. _____

G. _____  H. _____  I. _____

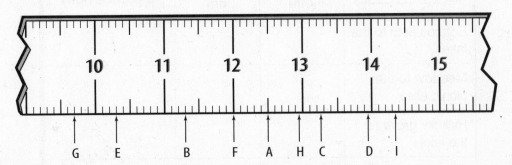

## Using Metric Measurements to Find Surface Area and Volume

Surface area of a rectangle = length × width

Volume of a rectangular prism = length × width × height

Volume of a cylinder = $\pi \times radius^2 \times height$

*Your teacher will give you several objects, including those items listed in **Table 1**. Using your metric ruler, make the required measurements and complete the table. Use your data to calculate surface area or volume for each item.*

**Table 1**

| Object | Length | Width | Height | Surface area/volume |
|---|---|---|---|---|
| Index card | | | | |
| Microscopic slide | | | | |
| Petri dish | | | | |
| Chalk | | | | |
| Desk top | | | | |
| | | | | |
| | | | | |

# Measurement Skill

## Using a Metric Scale

*Using your metric ruler and the map below, measure the distances between the center of the points indicated in **Table 1**. Record your answers in the table. Complete the table using the scale 10 cm = 1 km.*

**Table 1**

| How far is it from the_____? | Metric measurement | | Actual distance (km) |
|---|---|---|---|
| | mm | cm | |
| Softball field to the lake | | | |
| Meadow to the picnic area | | | |
| Hickory grove to the lake | | | |
| Pine forest to the picnic area | | | |
| Softball field to the hickory grove | | | |
| Softball field to the lake through the meadow | | | |

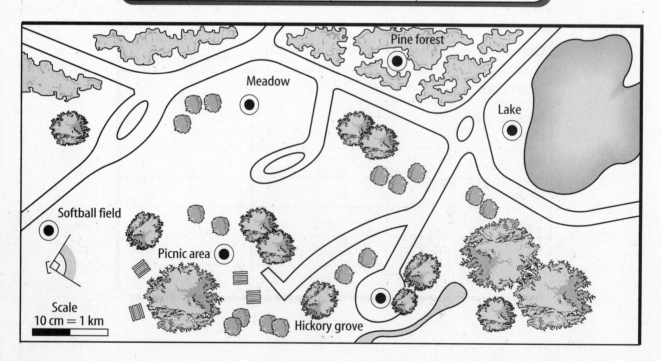

# SECTION 23 Measurement Skill

## Measuring with a Microscope

*Part 1*

Microscopes are optical instruments, much like a pair of glasses. The purpose of the microscope is to help you see things that are very small. The microscope can introduce you to organisms that you otherwise would not see.

*First, identify the parts of the microscope shown in **Figure 1** on the lines to the left.*

**Figure 1: Parts of the microscope**

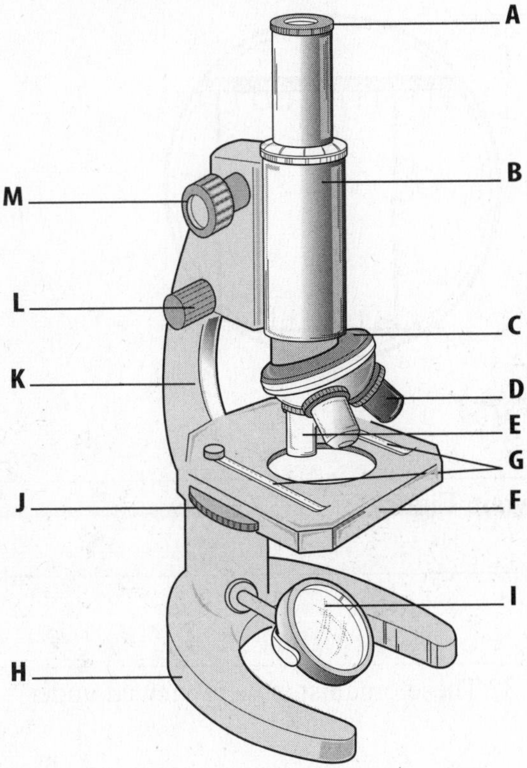

A. _____

B. _____

C. _____

D. _____

E. _____

F. _____

G. _____

H. _____

I. _____

J. _____

K. _____

L. _____

M. _____

*Part 2*

Because a microscope is a delicate instrument, it requires careful handling.

*Show that you are aware of how to handle a microscope correctly by completing the following statements.*

**1.** Always carry a microscope with one hand on the _____

and the other hand on the _____ .

**2.** A microscope should be stored with the _____ objective in place.

**3.** Always bring a specimen into focus using the _____ objective.

**4.** NEVER use the _____ adjustment to focus the high power objective.

*Activity 23, continued*

**5.** Do not allow direct sunlight to fall on the _____.

**6.** Use only the _____ adjustment when focusing with the high-power objective.

**7.** Lenses should be cleaned with _____.

*Part 3*

The size of microscopic organisms can be estimated using the method given here.

*Study the information below and fill in the blanks for items 1–4.*

The approximate size of the field of view seen under low power can be determined by actual measurement. A transparent millimeter ruler is placed across the field of view as shown in **Figure 2**.

**Figure 2: Low-power magnification**

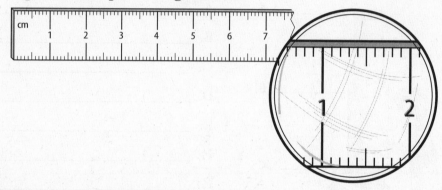

**1.** How many millimeters wide is the field of view shown?

_____

**2.** How many microns wide is the low power field shown in **Figure 2**?

_____

**3.** What is the width of the high power field of view?

_____

**4.** What is the width of the organisms shown in **Figure 3**? These organisms were viewed under high power.

**Figure 3: High-power magnification**

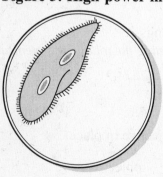  

**A.** _____    **B.** _____    **C.** _____

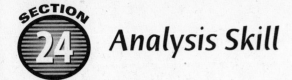

# Analysis Skill

## Making a Table

As you study science, you will find that often information is presented in a table. You also will organize data and observations in tables. You will be asked to use information given in tables. Knowing how to make and use tables is an important skill.

Tables have a title, rows, columns, and heads. The title is found at the top of the table. The title tells you what information is contained in the table. Columns are the sections that run up and down. At the top of each column is a head that tells you what information is in the column. Rows are sections that run from one side to another on the table.

*Use the information in the paragraph below to complete Table 1.*

When you complete a table, you must record the information in the proper columns and rows. There are approximately 5,000 known, living species in Phylum Porifera; 9,000 species in Phylum Cnidaria; 41,000 species in the nine main phyla of worms; 50,000 species in Phylum Mollusca; 879,000 species in Phylum Arthropoda; 44,000 species in Phylum Chordata; and 6,000 species in Phylum Echinodermata.

**Table 1**

| Number of Animal Species ||
|---|---|
| **Phylum** | **Number** |
|  |  |
|  |  |
|  |  |
|  |  |
|  |  |
|  |  |
|  |  |

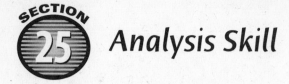

## SECTION 25

# *Analysis Skill*

## Making a Bar Graph

Bar graphs are useful for showing comparisons. A bar graph always has two axes, a horizontal and a vertical axis—and these axes are labeled and divided.

**Table 1**

| Selected Deserts of the World | |
|---|---|
| **Desert** | **Area (km²)** |
| Atacama | 181,300 |
| Gobi | 1,295,000 |
| Great Arabian | 920,100 |
| Great Australian | 1,091,400 |
| Sahara | 1,424,500 |

**Source:** *New York Times 1999 Almanac*

*Plot the data from **Table 1** on the bar graph below. The bar for Atacama has been done for you.*

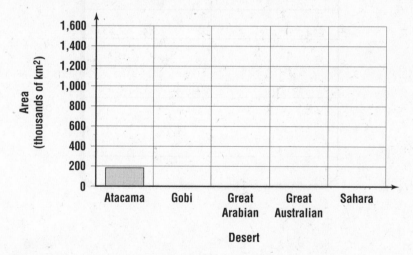

**Source:** *The New York Times 1999 Almanac*

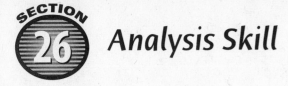

# Analysis Skill

## Making a Line Graph

Line graphs show data plotted as points that are connected by a line. Line graphs often are used to show change. You also can use line graphs to compare changes over time between two or more sets of data.

The size of the U.S. population between the ages of 35 and 44 is shown on the line graph below. Use the population data for people between the ages of 14 and 17 in **Table 1** to plot a comparison. Use a different color or line pattern.

**Table 1**

| U.S. Population Between the Ages of 14 and 17 ||
| Year | Population (thousands) |
| --- | --- |
| 1960 | 11,219 |
| 1970 | 15,924 |
| 1980 | 16,142 |
| 1990* | 13,311 |
| 2000* | 15,752 |

\* population estimated
**Source:** *U.S. Bureau of the Census*

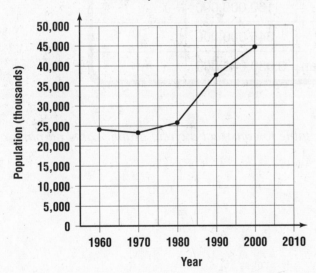

**U.S. Population by Age Group**

1. Which of the two age groups' populations changed the most?

_____

2. During which time period did it increase? Decrease?_____

_____

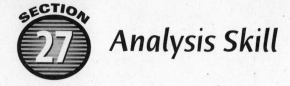

# Analysis Skill

## Making a Circle Graph

Circle graphs show how each part is related to the whole.

_Use the data from the **Table** below to make a circle graph. Calculate the fractional amount of time for each of the sections._

The total circle will represent 4.6 billion years. To find the fraction for each section, divide the time length of that section by 4,600,000,000. Then multiply the fraction by 360 degrees to determine the angle for the section. The calculation for the Cenozoic Era is given.

$$65,000,000 \text{ years} \div \text{ by } 4,600,000,000 \text{ years} = 0.0141 \times 360° = 5.09°$$

Round the final answer to the nearest whole degree. Use this procedure to complete **Table 1**.

**Table 1**

| Era | Number of years | Number of degrees |
|---|---|---|
| Cenozoic | 65,000,000 | 5 |
| Mesozoic | 160,000,000 | |
| Paleozoic | 345,000,000 | |
| Precambrian | 3,930,000,000 | |

_Use a protractor and the data from the table to construct a circle graph. Label all parts of the graph._

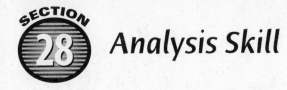

# Analysis Skill

## Using a Scientific Method

Scientists are interested in the world around them. This curiosity leads them to investigate things and events. Scientists use their senses to observe as they investigate. They use many methods of scientific problem solving. One scientific problem-solving technique has six steps:

1. State the problem.
2. Gather information about the problem.
3. Form a hypothesis.
4. Test the hypothesis.
5. Accept or reject the hypothesis.
6. Do something with the results.

*Read the information in the paragraph and answer the following questions, applying the scientific method outlined in the box.*

Scientists observed that white mice that were fed seeds appeared to grow more than mice given leafy green and yellow vegetables. The scientists hypothesized that the protein in the seeds was responsible for the growth. They designed an experiment to test this hypothesis. They divided 200 mice of the same age, size, health, and sex into two groups of 100 mice each. The mice were kept under identical conditions for 14 days. One group was given a diet low in protein. The other group was given a normal protein diet. The mass of each mouse was recorded daily for 14 days.

1. Which group of mice served as a control?

_____

2. What was the variable?

_____

3. What effect of the protein diet was tested?

_____

_____

4. What other effects of a protein diet could have been tested?

_____

_____

5. Why were larger numbers of mice used in this experiment?

_____

_____

6. If the results of the experiment did not show a marked change between the two groups, what should the scientists do next?

_____

7. What are the parts of an experiment?

_____

_____

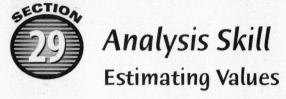

# Analysis Skill
## Estimating Values

The ability to estimate values such as length, mass, volume, and temperature is a useful skill. This skill can serve as a quick check of your answers to problems. For example, suppose that your bedroom is approximately 13 m² and your classroom is approximately 130 m². If you measured the length and width of your bedroom and calculated the area to be 130 m², an estimate of the answer would serve as a way of checking the placement of your decimal point.

*For the questions in Part 1, estimate the values using SI units for each example listed. Check your answers by either making the measurements yourself or using data your teacher provides. After answering the questions in Part 1, estimate the values for the items listed in Part 2 on the next page and then check your answers. Compare your estimates in Parts 1 and 2 and answer the remaining questions.*

*Part 1*

| **Making Estimates** | **Estimated values** | **Actual values** |
|---|---|---|
| **1.** How long, tall, or far is it? | | |
| **a.** a paper clip | _____ | _____ |
| **b.** your teacher | _____ | _____ |
| **c.** from Los Angeles to New York City | _____ | _____ |
| **d.** from your home to your school | _____ | _____ |
| **2.** How much matter does it contain? | | |
| **a.** one chocolate chip | _____ | _____ |
| **b.** a soda cracker | _____ | _____ |
| **c.** a newborn baby | _____ | _____ |
| **d.** your science book | _____ | _____ |
| **3.** How much liquid will it hold? | | |
| **a.** a school milk container | _____ | _____ |
| **b.** a soft drink can | _____ | _____ |
| **c.** a teaspoon | _____ | _____ |
| **d.** a coffee cup | _____ | _____ |
| **4.** How hot or cold is it? (Use °C.) | | |
| **a.** when water freezes | _____ | _____ |
| **b.** your normal body temperature | _____ | _____ |
| **c.** comfortable room temperature | _____ | _____ |
| **d.** on a hot, August day | _____ | _____ |

**5.** For which type of estimation were your answers the most accurate?

_____

**6.** For which type of estimation were your answers the least accurate?

_____

*Activity 29, continued*

**7.** Why do you think some types of estimation are easier for you than others?

_____

_____

*Part 2*

| **Making Estimates** | **Estimated values** | **Actual values** |
|---|---|---|

**1.** How long, tall, or far is it?

|   |   |   |   |
|---|---|---|---|
| **a.** a new pencil | | _____ | _____ |
| **b.** a pine needle | | _____ | _____ |
| **c.** a newborn baby | | _____ | _____ |
| **d.** from Los Angeles to Dallas | | _____ | _____ |

**2.** How much matter does it contain?

|   |   |   |
|---|---|---|
| **a.** a potato chip | _____ | _____ |
| **b.** a cat | _____ | _____ |
| **c.** a candy bar | _____ | _____ |
| **d.** a ten-speed bicycle | _____ | _____ |

**3.** How much liquid will it hold?

|   |   |   |
|---|---|---|
| **a.** a drinking glass | _____ | _____ |
| **b.** a straw | _____ | _____ |
| **c.** a baby bottle | _____ | _____ |
| **d.** a punch bowl | _____ | _____ |

**4.** How hot or cold is it? (Use °C.)

|   |   |   |
|---|---|---|
| **a.** when water boils | _____ | _____ |
| **b.** inside your refrigerator | _____ | _____ |
| **c.** a cup of hot tea | _____ | _____ |
| **d.** during a snowstorm | _____ | _____ |

**5.** For which types of values did your estimation improve the most?

_____

_____

**6.** List three ways you can use estimation to help you in everyday activities.

_____

_____

_____

**7.** What other activities could you do to help develop your estimation skills?

_____

_____

# Safety Skill

## Identifying Improper Safety Practices

*The pictures below show students performing laboratory activities incorrectly. Study each picture and write in the space provided all improper laboratory techniques that are illustrated. Be prepared to explain why it is important to follow each safety procedure.*

1. _____

_____

2. _____

_____

# Safety Skill

## Correcting Unsafe Practices

*Explain what is wrong in each of the following illustrations and tell how to correct it.*

**1.** Error _____

Correction_____

_____

_____

**2.** Error _____

Correction _____

_____

_____

**3.** Error _____

Correction _____

_____

_____

*Activity 31, continued*

**4.** Error _____

Correction _____

_____

_____

**5.** Error _____

Correction _____

_____

_____

**6.** Error _____

Correction _____

_____

_____

# Safety Skill

## Developing Safety Policies

*Several statements are printed in **Column I** concerning students' activities and attitudes in the laboratory. Think about each statement and formulate a safety rule or procedure related to each statement. Write one or two clear, concise sentences in **Column II** that can serve as a safety policy for your science classroom.*

**Column I**

**Column II**

1. Stephanie says that her teacher is solely responsible for preventing laboratory accidents.

1. _____
_____
_____
_____
_____

2. Keshia started the lab activity before reading it through completely.

2. _____
_____
_____
_____
_____

3. Ricardo decided to do a lab activity that he read in a library book before the teacher came into the classroom.

3. _____
_____
_____
_____
_____

4. Hal says that the lab aprons are unattractive and that the safety goggles mess up his hair. He refuses to wear them.

4. _____
_____
_____
_____
_____

# Safety Skill

## Using Safety Devices Correctly

*Describe the location and purpose of having each of the following devices in your science laboratory. Write your answers in the spaces provided. (Locations will vary according to your laboratory's design.)*

**1.** fire blanket

_____

_____

_____

_____

**2.** $CO_2$ fire extinguisher

_____

_____

_____

_____

**3.** goggles

_____

_____

_____

_____

**4.** eyewash station

_____

_____

_____

_____

**5.** safety hood or vent

_____

_____

_____

_____

# Managing the Laboratory Day-by-Day

## Managing Student Lab Work

### Before a Lab Session

Before students begin a lab session, familiarize yourself with the activity to be performed so that you know how the lab needs to be set up and what materials to have on hand. If you are not familiar with the activity, do a trial run so that you'll be better able to help students conduct it. You'll also need to be prepared to enforce all safety rules (see pp. 15) and allow sufficient cleanup time.

### *Lab and Materials Setup*

- Make sure that safety and evacuation guidelines are posted.
- Be sure safety equipment (pp. 138–141) is accessible and working.
- Arrange the lab in such a way that equipment and supplies are clearly labeled and easily and safely accessible.
- Set up only the equipment and materials that are needed to complete the assigned activity. (Note: this practice helps eliminate the problem of students doing unauthorized investigations.)
- Check that all investigation equipment is in good condition (no cracks in glassware, no frayed electrical cords, and so forth) (see pp. 18–22).
- Set up beakers or widemouthed jars and droppers for any solutions and reagents that will be used. **WARNING:** *Remind students to use a separate dropper for each solution. Do NOT return leftover chemicals to their original containers.*
- Arrange for proper disposal of wastes prior to the investigation (see p. 83).
- Know all actions and reactions that should occur between the chemicals to be used and investigate unexpected reactions that might occur. Refer to the Material Safety Data Sheet for each substance to be used. Highlight all safety concerns about the substance. See pp. 118–121 for a sample MSDS with safety issues highlighted.
- Dilute solutions of chemicals should be used when possible.

*Preparing Kits* If you are planning a series of lab activities that use similar materials and if you have an adequate supply of them, you may wish to set up kits for students using plastic tubs or cardboard shoeboxes as containers for the materials. Each kit should contain an equipment checklist for the students to use such as the one that follows.

Group/student _____ Date _____

| Quantity | Description | Breakage |
|----------|-------------|----------|
| 2 | beaker (25 mL) | |
| 2 | beaker (50 mL) | |
| 1 | graduated cylinder (25 mL) | |
| 1 | burner | |
| 2 | collecting bottle | |
| 2 | dropper | |

Date kit checked out _____ Date kit checked in _____

Have each team of students be responsible for filling out and returning this checklist to you at specific intervals. These lists will enable you not only to keep track of materials and breakage, but also to assess students' proficiency in keeping their equipment organized and in good shape.

Equipment and specimens that are used only a few times during the course should be labeled and stored in containers in a storage area separate from students' kits. (See pp. 134.)

## Trial Run

- Always read/re-read an investigation carefully.
- Analyze the investigation for appropriateness for your students.
- Determine approximately how long the investigation will take an average student to perform.
- Anticipate what could go wrong during a typical laboratory activity and take steps to reduce the probability.
- Perform the activity yourself so that you can determine where students may have trouble.
- Consider substitute chemicals or procedures if they will be more appropriate or safer. Refer to the Material Safety Data Sheet (MSDS) (see pp. 117–121) and the Chemical Incompatibility Reference Sheet (pp. 125–126) for each substance to be used to be sure the substitutions will be safe and will work as planned.

## During a Lab Session

### Getting Students Started

- Be sure students know proper procedures to follow if an accident should occur. (See pp. 91–92.)
- Require that students are wearing appropriate clothing and the protective equipment indicated for the planned lab activity (see pp. 17).
- At the beginning of each laboratory session, remind students to follow safe practices. (See pp. 15.) Explain the consequences that will be enforced for unsafe behavior.
- Instruct students to follow directions carefully in the order they are presented and NOT to take short cuts. (Short cuts may lead to unsafe conditions and unsuccessful investigations.)
- Go over all the safety precautions found in the lab activity. Make sure students' hands and work areas are dry.
- Make sure that students have only those items needed for the assigned lab activity in their work areas.
- Demonstrate the proper use of the devices to be used for the lab activity. Review with students the procedures for proper use of the equipment needed for the assigned lab activity. (See pp. 18–22 and 30–60.)
- Distribute the Pre-Lab and Post-Lab worksheet found on p. 88. Assign the Pre-Lab portion of the worksheet.
- Discuss the Pre-Lab worksheet and answer students' questions regarding the lab activity.
- Check students' laboratory designs and setups before giving them permission to start the lab activity procedure.

### As Students Work

- Monitor the lab and students continuously to foster safe learning.
- Work with students to correct any procedure or action that is not safe.

- If accidents do occur, follow school/district guidelines on first aid and reporting the accident (see pp. 94–97 and 104).

### After a Lab Activity

*Post-Lab Work* Assign the Post-Lab portion of the Pre-Lab and Post-Lab worksheet found on p. 88. Discuss the responses with students and clear up any misconceptions that might still exist regarding the lab activity.

### Cleanup Procedures

- Distribute to students the checklist of cleanup procedures found on p. 89. You may wish to post the checklist as a daily reminder.
- Direct students to clean up their work areas and as they do so, inspect all devices for problems. Make sure the devices are clean and dry before you store them. Also make sure chemical containers are clean and properly labeled before you return them to storage.
- Disinfect work surfaces at least once after each class and after any spill of active cultures. A solution of 10 percent household bleach and 90 percent water may be used to disinfect.
- All liquid and solid wastes that are contaminated must be decontaminated before disposal. These wastes may be sterilized with steam or by soaking them in a 10 percent bleach solution for one hour.
- Culture plates of bacteria collected by students, including bacteria in soil, should remain sealed and then be sterilized before disposal.
- After working with radioisotopes, monitor the lab area, equipment, and persons present in the lab for contamination.
- Sterilize scalpels and dissecting instruments before and after investigations.
- Follow all regulations regarding the disposal of waste materials that produce radiation.

# Maintaining an Environmentally Safe Laboratory

## Waste Disposal Guidelines

This section deals with daily cleanup needs and temporary storage of waste products. See pp. 129–130 for information regarding waste reduction measures and major reorganization and cleanup of old and excess quantities of chemicals.

Work with your custodial department regarding how to store waste and where the waste goes after it leaves the classroom laboratory. Keep school administration and local officials, such as the fire department, informed as to the location of waste stored temporarily and your waste disposal procedures. **WARNING:** *Most states place a limit on the volume of chemicals that may be stored in school facilities. Know what your state and local regulations are.*

Use separate containers for different kinds of waste—paper trash, broken glass, biohazardous materials, sharp objects contaminated with biohazardous fluids, toxic or caustic waste, and so forth. **WARNING:** *Mixed waste that contains safe and hazardous substances is considered hazardous.* Equipment supply companies have proper containers. Make sure the containers have the proper labels with safety icons and that students recognize the labels. **WARNING:** *Do NOT stack the containers as leaks must be visible, ensuring prompt corrective action.*

*Broken Glassware* Clean up broken glassware immediately. Set aside gloves, brush, and dustpan for that purpose. Wet cotton balls are effective in picking up tiny pieces of glass.

*Batteries* Batteries are caustic and should be kept separate from paper trash. **WARNING:** *Do NOT incinerate batteries. They are explosive.*

*Mercury* **WARNING:** *Mercury thermometers are NOT recommended. If you still use them, clean up spills according to the following steps.*

- *On a hard surface,* while you're wearing gloves, use either a stiff paper to brush the beads together or a dropper to collect the beads. Put all parts— the broken thermometer, the paper or dropper, and the beads of mercury—in a widemouth jar. Seal the jar and place it in the toxic/caustic waste container for proper disposal.
- *On a carpet,* the mercury spill should be cut out and disposed of in a toxic/caustic container. **WARNING:** *Do NOT vacuum the mercury because it will cause the mercury to evaporate and become a part of the atmosphere. Incinerating mercury also will cause it to become part of the atmosphere.*
- When you replace mercury thermometers with digital ones, dispose of the mercury thermometers as you would a mercury spill.

### Other Chemicals

- Many chemicals may be washed down the sink. For example, almost all sodium compounds may be washed down the drain. Refer to water treatment officials for guidelines—they probably recommend that all liquid waste be adjusted to a pH between 5 and 8.
- Any waste that must not be washed down the drain should be kept in safe containers. Empty reagent bottles with plastic coating are suitable for most liquid waste. Solid waste can be discarded in empty chemical jars. **WARNING:** *All stored waste MUST be labeled. Waste disposal costs rise for unknown substances.*
- **WARNING:** *UNKNOWN substances may NOT be disposed of in the water or land. See pp. 130–131 regarding procedures for disposing of unknown substances.*

### Biological Contamination

- Biological specimens and bandages, towels, and gloves used in cleaning up blood and other bodily fluids should be placed in the red biohazard containers and disposed of properly.
- Sharp items such as needles and scalpel blades should be placed in a red biohazard container made especially for sharp objects.
- Glassware and microscope slides can be sterilized and reused. See p. 85.

## Sterilization Procedures

Eyewear MUST be cleaned if it is shared or if the wearer has an infection. Clean glassware is necessary to keep from contaminating an experiment and to provide safe equipment for students to use.

*Goggles* Germicidal ultraviolet (UV) cabinets are available. If used, follow the manufacturer's instructions. Check the UV intensity yearly with a UV meter. Clean the lamp often (weekly) as dust and dirt will affect the intensity of the lamp. One drawback to the UV cabinet is the time it takes for the sterilization to be effective. An alternative method follows.

1. Clean the goggles, frame, and lenses with liquid detergent on a paper towel. Rinse the goggles with water and partially dry with a paper towel. Use a separate paper towel for each pair of goggles.
2. Dip the goggles into a solution of one tablespoon of household bleach and one quart of water or wipe the goggles with a gauze pad or cotton ball soaked with a 70 percent isopropyl alcohol solution. *Note:* a bleach solution should be made fresh daily.
3. Let the goggles air-dry.
4. *In case of an infection,* the goggles should be soaked in the bleach solution for 10 min following the washing with a liquid detergent. This bleach solution should be discarded and not used for anyone else's goggles.

## Glassware

- Glassware should be washed immediately. If that is not possible, soak the glassware until it can be washed.
- Most glassware can be cleaned with detergents and brushes. The glassware should be washed thoroughly with detergent and rinsed several times, with a final rinse of distilled water. (If all the detergent is not removed with the rinsing, the detergent will react with acids to form a grease coating on the glassware.) **WARNING:** *Do NOT use worn brushes with exposed metal that can scratch the glass.*
- Various methods may be used to sterilize glassware.
  - *Dry heat.* Larger pieces of glassware (petri dishes, beakers, graduated cylinders, test tubes) may be sterilized by placing them in an oven at a temperature of 160–190°C for 2 h.
  - *Steam under pressure.* Place media or glassware in a pressure cooker or autoclave for 15 min. **WARNING:** *Do NOT open the cover until you turn off the heat source and allow the pressure to return to normal.*
  - *Boiling.* Smaller pieces of glassware (droppers, stirring rods, and so forth) may be sterilized by boiling them in water for 30 min.
  - *Using chemicals.* Culture dishes can be soaked in a 10 percent solution of household bleach and then rinsed with water, finishing with a rinse with distilled water. **WARNING:** *Wear rubber gloves to avoid burns when using strong disinfectants.* **WARNING:** *Some residues are not affected by detergents.* Alcoholic KOH dissolves many organic substances that are NOT water-soluble. Trisodium phosphate and dichromate acid react with substances to make water-soluble products. *Note:* Dichromate acid and alcoholic KOH are NOT normally used for sterilization, but may result in sterilization. **WARNING:** *These substances are hazardous and should be handled carefully.* **WARNING:** *Trisodium phosphate may actually serve as a nutrient for microbes.*

## Blackline Masters Divider

# Pre-Lab Worksheet

**Name of Lab** _____ **Date** _____

**1.** What science concept is this lab about?

**2.** Strategies:
What materials/devices will I use? (Test tubes? Graduated cylinder? Metric ruler? Chemicals?)
Where will I find the materials in the laboratory?
Do I need a partner for this investigation? If so, who will do what job? (Measure? Record data?)
Do I need a data table? What will the heads be?
Do I need a graph? What type of graph? (Line? Bar? Circle?)

**3.** What laboratory skills will I use during the investigation? (Measure with a graduate cylinder? Use a hot plate? Measure the mass or volume of a substance? Measure the temperature of a liquid?)

**4.** In what order will I use the skills described above?

**5.** What safety precautions do I have to take?

**6.** What results do I expect from this investigation?

**7.** What am I expected to do about cleanup when the investigation is done?

# Post-Lab Worksheet

**Name of Lab** _____ **Date** _____

**1.** If I did not get the results I expected, what was the source of error and why did it occur?

**2.** What changes would I make in the procedure?

**3.** What further investigations could I do to get a good understanding of the main concept?

# Student Laboratory Cleanup Checklist

_____ Promptly clean up your work area while still wearing your protective equipment.

_____ Turn off all hot plates or burners.

_____ Unplug electrical devices.

_____ Place all waste items in the proper disposal containers. NEVER wash anything down the sink drain unless instructed to do so by your teacher.

_____ Wash glassware with warm water and detergent. Then rinse the glassware several times with water, with a final rinse of distilled water.

_____ Wash the surface of your worktable.

_____ Return laboratory devices to their storage area as directed by your teacher, carrying them properly.

_____ Wash your gloved hands with warm water and soap, being careful not to get water on the inside of your gloves.

_____ Remove the gloves by peeling them off your hands—start at the wrist and keep working toward the fingers. Do NOT let the outside surface of the glove contact the skin. Dispose of the gloves as directed by your teacher.

_____ After you have removed your gloves, wash your hands in warm soapy water. Do NOT touch doorknobs, telephones, textbooks, your goggles, or other items until after you have removed your gloves and washed your hands.

_____ Remove your safety goggles after you have washed your hands.

_____ Wash and sterilize your goggles according to your teacher's instructions.

# Responding to Emergencies

Many of the tools and chemicals in the science laboratory can cause injury or allergic reactions if used without proper attention and care. Allergic reactions can be in the form of swelling or hives, muscle cramps, disorientation, unconsciousness, and death from shock or suffocation. Even with the best efforts at prevention, emergencies still occur. Therefore, along with practicing effective safety measures, you also must be prepared to act according to the given situation.

Obtain medical help in every case of serious injury or illness, in all cases of injury to the eye, and whenever in doubt. **WARNING:** *A teacher should NOT diagnose or treat injury or illness, or offer medication, but may offer the necessary first aid until medical help is obtained.* After emergencies are contained, file an accident report whenever there is any injury to a student and/or property damage, even if it is not required (see p. 104 for a sample form).

## Very First Steps

In cases of emergency, seemingly different responses need to take place simultaneously—calling 911, getting the school nurse, using the safety equipment, administering first aid, and so forth. Memorize the following first steps as they pertain to different kinds of emergencies.

1. **Keep calm** in all cases and **call 911**.
2. **In case of injury**, send a student to get the school nurse, if available, or principal.
   - If the victim is not breathing, restore breathing if you have the training to do so.
   - Stop any bleeding by applying a light pressure, wearing protective gloves. **WARNING:** *If an object lies in the wound, do NOT remove the object.*
   - Prevent shock. A clean fire blanket is useful for keeping an accident victim warm to help prevent shock (see pp. 93 and 140).
   - Contact the parent or guardian as soon as possible.
3. **In case of fire,** begin evacuation and sound the alarm immediately.
4. **In case of chemical spill,** place affected student in the safety shower or use eyewash station if the spill affects the eyes (see p. 93).

## First Steps in Detail

### In Case of Injury

If a student receives a wound that causes severe bleeding or if the student is unconscious, send for the nurse and call 911. If the injury is severe but the victim is ambulatory, accompany the person to the nurse's office. The nurse should:

- administer additional first aid.
- contact the parent or guardian of the injured person.
- pursue additional treatment.

If a nurse is not available, the teacher must:

- contact the parent or guardian and advise him or her of the severity of the accident and obtain permission from the parent or guardian to proceed with treatment as needed.

If a parent or guardian cannot be reached, the teacher must act in accordance with the situation. If an emergency medical form (see p. 103) exists which grants permission for emergency health care to be administered, a physician should be called and, upon the physician's advice, seek treatment for the injured student.

Emergencies

### In Case of Shock

Causes of shock include electrical charges from equipment and outlets and from lightning and severe allergic reactions and other illnesses. A person suffering from shock may be unconscious or dazed, weak, and confused, or may even stop breathing.

- Call for emergency medical aid immediately.
- Check for breathing and pulse immediately.
- Keep the injured person warm, quiet, and lying down. Elevate the feet a few inches if there are no chest or head injuries.
- Start CPR if necessary.
- If the shock is from electricity, separate the person from the electrical source carefully. **WARNING:** *Make sure you have dry hands and are not standing on a wet floor.* **WARNING:** *Do NOT use a metal object or other conducting material to separate the victim from the power source.*
- Use the master control switch to shut off the electricity.
- Check for entrance and exit burns. Treat burns as you would a thermal burn. Two burns may be present—one where the power entered the body and the other where it exited. Some burns may be large and below the skin. See pp. 94–97 for first aid measures.

### In Case of Fire

- Evacuate the students, sound the fire alarm, shut off master switches in the classroom for gas and electrical power (if available), close windows and doors if possible, and then determine whether it is feasible to try to put the fire out. Be informed regarding which type of fire extinguisher to use (see p. 140) and the proper use of fire blankets (see p. 93). **WARNING:** *If the fire is spreading or could block the escape route, leave immediately and let professionals fight the fire.*
- Cloth towels or fire blankets may be used to smother a small fire.
- Inform students of the priority to first *stop*, then *drop*, and then *roll* in putting out clothing fires.
- **WARNING:** *Do NOT use a fire extinguisher on a person as serious chemical burns or frostbite can result.*

### In Case of Chemical Spills

If a chemical spill occurs in the laboratory or in the classroom, quick action can reduce the possibility of injury to a student or teacher. A chemical spill such as a liter bottle of hydrochloric acid breaking in the chemistry laboratory is considered a major spill.

- Immediately evacuate all students through the exits farthest from the spill. Fumes from a chemical spill can cause severe damage to the body.
- Immediately assist any person splashed with the chemical to the safety shower (see pp. 93).
- Turn on the emergency exhaust fan.
- Contain the spill wearing the proper protective clothing. **WARNING:** *Do NOT allow the spill to trap you.*
- Call for help. The school safety plan should contain the numbers of agencies or departments in your community that will assist in containment and removal of the chemical.
- For materials entering the eye—rush to the eye wash station. The first response prior to medical treatment, for a student or teacher who has hazardous material in the eye, is flushing with water to dilute chemicals,

wash out debris, or irrigate the eyes. (See below for techniques for using the eyewash station.)
- In case of mercury spills, provide maximum ventilation and avoid all contact with skin, clothing, or shoes. See pp. 94–98 for measures regarding cleanup.
- In case of biological contamination, use gloves during first aid and in cleaning up blood and other bodily fluids. See p. 84. for material on the proper disposal of contaminated items.

# Using Accident Response Equipment

## Eyewash Stations
- Begin washing the face, eyelids, and eyes for at least 15 min as soon as possible. The eyelids should be held open, rotating the eyes as much as possible so water can flow on all surfaces and in the folds surrounding the eyeballs to ensure removal of the chemical.
- **WARNING**: *Do NOT rely on spray bottles as a substitute for eyewash stations.*
- **WARNING**: *Contact lenses, if worn, should be removed immediately if at all possible. Continue flushing even if contacts cannot be removed.*
- If the injured person is lying down, gently hold the eyelids open and pour water from the inner corner of the eye outward. **WARNING:** *Do NOT allow the chemical to run into the other eye.*
- In the case of an alkaline burn or any other serious eye injury, immediately send for an ambulance so that first aid will not have to be discontinued during transport to medical facilities.

## Safety Showers
- Begin use of the shower as soon as possible, removing any contaminated clothing while in the shower (have large towels or lab coats available for privacy).
- The victim should remain in the shower for a minimum of 15 min, washing the skin with water or with soap and water for some organic chemical splashes. Cooler water is fine; it slows chemical reactions and is good first aid for burns.
- **WARNING:** *AVOID use of neutralizing solutions unless recommended by medical personnel.*

## Fire Blankets
To use a fire blanket, follow the manufacturer's recommended technique of wrapping the victim in it to extinguish the fire. **WARNING:** *Incorrect use could hold heat in near the body, increasing the possibility of burns.*

- *For a folded fire blanket stored in a case:*
  - The blanket should be spread on the floor so that the person whose hair or clothing is on fire can wrap it around the body while rolling.
- *For a fire blanket in a vertical wall case:*
  - the blanket will unroll from the case as the person whose hair or clothing is on fire wraps the blanket around his or her body. As soon as the blanket is out of the case, the person should lie on the floor to prevent a "chimney effect."

In both cases, the blanket should be held closely at the neck to force flames away from the head.

### First Aid Kits

Students should be aware of the location of the first aid kit, but a teacher should be the one to administer first aid. First aid kits should be kept in a conspicuous place in the classroom or laboratory. This location should be marked clearly. See p. 141 for equipping first aid kits.

# Giving First Aid

First aid is the first assistance provided to a person suffering an accident or a sudden illness. Persons giving first aid should seek NOT to treat the victim but to protect him or her until professional medical assistance arrives. Every teacher bears the responsibility for knowing how to help a student in the case of an accident or illness.

Teachers are highly recommended to take a first aid course with CPR training. Some states require that at least some teachers in a school be formally trained in first aid. Check school regulations regarding the training of students in using emergency equipment, such as the safety showers and eyewash stations. **WARNING:** *Gloves should be worn by anyone administering first aid.*

This section provides general procedures for injuries most commonly related to school laboratory work. Most injuries are minor cuts and burns to the hand. Many injuries occur when students are cleaning glassware. In addition to the possibility of injury from broken glass, there is the threat of injury from the cleaning solution or chemical substance used with the glassware.

### Cuts and Scratches

- Wash the injured area thoroughly.
- Place a compress on the wound to stop the flow of blood. **WARNING:** *Do NOT disturb blood clotting by removing saturated cloth, simply add more layers.*
- Replace a compress with a sterile bandage if the injury is minor. **WARNING:** *Do NOT use any topical medications unless advised to do so by a physician.*
- Accompany the student to the nurse's office if he or she has a moderate to severe injury.
- **WARNING:** *In case of severe cuts, do NOT use a tourniquet unless you are trained to do so and then only as a last resort.*
- Follow proper procedures to clean up blood (see pp. 83–84 and 98–99).

### Seizures, Fainting Spells, Concussions, and Shock

- Leave the person lying down. Loosen any tight clothing and keep crowds away. Call the nurse immediately.
- Call for emergency medical aid immediately.
- Check for breathing and pulse immediately.
- Keep the injured person warm, quiet, and lying down. Elevate the feet a few inches if there are no chest or head injuries.
- Start CPR if necessary.

### Injuries from Chemical Spills

- Rush the injured person to the safety shower. Immediately drench the entire injured area with a continuous flow of water. (see p. 93).
- Send a student to alert the school nurse or to get another teacher.
- Use a spill kit to contain and remove the chemicals (see pp. 98 and 141).

### Eye Injuries from Foreign Substances

- Rush the student to the dual eyewash station. Remember to guide the student as he or she will have difficulty seeing.
- Rinse the open eyes with a continuous stream of water for 15 min. (See p. 93.)
- Send a student to alert the school nurse or another teacher.

### Exposure to Toxic Substances

- Rush the person to the nurse's office and call 911. The person calling for medical assistance should know the victim's age and weight, the poison involved, the amount taken, whether any first aid has been given, whether the victim has vomited, and how long it will take to get the victim to the hospital.
- The nurse should also contact the Poison Control Center immediately.
- If CPR is required, a mouth-to-mask resuscitator should be used to protect the person administering aid from succumbing to the hazardous substance as well.
- **WARNING:** *Toxic substances may enter the body by inhalation, ingestion, injection, or skin contact.*

### Inhaled Poisons

- Call for medical assistance.
- Carry the victim to fresh air if possible. If the victim is too large to carry, open all doors and windows.
- Begin CPR if the victim is not breathing, but only if you are trained to do so. **WARNING:** *Do NOT inhale victim's breath.*
- Treat the victim for shock until medical assistance arrives. (See p. 94.)

### Ingested Poisons

- Consult the MSDS (see p. 117) filed in your department.
- Call for medical assistance.
- Maintain the victim's breathing.
- **WARNING:** Do NOT administer syrup of ipecac to induce vomiting, or water or milk for dilution of the poison, unless advised to do so by a physician or the Poison Control Center.
- Take the container of poison to the medical facility.

### Skin Contact Poisons

- Remove contaminated clothing as soon as possible if contact is made with a plant poison (such as poison ivy oils). Wear rubber gloves if you are helping a student. Immediately wash all exposed areas with large quantities of soap and water.
- See also section regarding the treatment of chemical burns of the skin and eyes (p. 96).

## Chemical Burns

If the chemical is a strong corrosive, irritant, or toxic, immediately send for an ambulance so that first aid will not have to be discontinued during transport to medical attention. This is especially important for strong alkali (such as sodium hydroxide) burns.

- Remove victim's clothing using rubber gloves.
- As quickly as possible, place the student in the safety shower for at least 15 minutes. (See pp. 93.)
- Call the nurse and 911.
- **WARNING:** *Do NOT attempt to neutralize the chemical unless approved by medical personnel and the chemical is first diluted with water.*
- Wash chemical burns to the eyes, eyelids, and face at the eyewash station for at least 15 min. (See pp. 93.)
- Remove contact lenses if at all possible.
- Cover burns with a sterile dressing (NOT fluff cotton).

## Thermal (Heat) Burns

Identify the severity (whether first-, second-, or third-degree) of the injury to the body and follow the appropriate first aid procedure.

*First-degree Burns* These are the least severe burns, affecting the outer layer of the epidermis only. They are characterized by redness and heat and commonly cause itching, burning, and pain in the victim.

- Hold burn under cool water for 5 min.
- Cover burn with a clean dressing.

*Second-degree Burns* These burns affect deeper layers of the epidermis. They are characterized by mottled red skin and blisters. Second-degree burns cause considerable pain and the loss of bodily fluids through blisters. The victim is at risk for infection and may require hospitalization.

- Lay clean towels over the burned areas and pour cool water over the towels. **WARNING:** *Do NOT add ice or salt to the water.*
- Gently blot the area dry. **WARNING:** *Do NOT break blisters, remove tissue, or apply any ointments, sprays, or salves.*
- Cover the burned area with a clean, dry dressing.
- **WARNING:** *If legs are affected, keep them elevated.*

*Third-degree Burns* These are the most severe burns, affecting skin as well as deeper tissue. Third-degree burns appear white or charred and cause little pain due to the damage caused to nerve endings. The victim may lose internal fluids and is at high risk for infection, and usually will require extensive hospitalization.

- Call 911.
- Call the school nurse.
- Treat for shock (see p. 94).
- **WARNING:** *Do NOT remove burnt clothing.*
- **WARNING:** *Do NOT cover burns with dressing.*

## Bites and Stings

- Wear gloves while attending bites. **WARNING:** *There is danger of infections and rabies from bites of all warm-blooded animals.*
- Identify the source of the bite or sting.

- If bites or stings are from venomous sources, seek medical help immediately.
- Keep victims calm and quiet. Keep injury area lower than the heart. **WARNING:** *Do NOT apply ice.*
- Call parents or guardians immediately.

**Venomous Snake Bites** **WARNING:** *Do NOT administer treatment unless a hospital is more than one hour away. If it is, then:*

- Apply constricting bands. Check pulse to be sure blood flow has not stopped.
- **WARNING:** *Incision and suction are NOT recommended.*
- If you have a field trip planned for an area where snakebite is possible and medical help will not be nearby, have a snake bite kit available and obtain training in its use.

**Tick Bites** Ticks should only be removed by parents or guardians. They should be contacted as soon as possible and advised to seek medical help, especially if the victim becomes ill within a week of the bite.

### In Case of Allergic Reactions

- Get immediate medical help if the victim has a history of allergies. (See p. 103 for a sample medical emergency form.)
- Keep the victim as quiet as possible.
- Use cold compresses (or ice wrapped in a cloth) to relieve swelling.
- Remove the stinger with a scraping motion with a stiff card or fingernail to reduce toxin injection. **WARNING:** *Do NOT pull the stinger out.*
- Wash the bite area with soap and water. Apply calamine lotion (or a paste of water and baking soda).
- Treat for shock if the allergic reaction is severe.
- **WARNING:** *Any sting to the throat, mouth, or tongue requires medical help immediately.*

### Human Bites

- Parents/guardians of both parties should be notified immediately. Medical records should be shared.
- Wash bite area with soap and water. Get medical treatment if the skin is broken.

## Cleaning Up Hazardous Spills

### Mercury

**WARNING:** Mercury thermometers are NOT recommended. If you still use them, and they break, use the following steps to clean up the spills.

- A mercury sponge, which contains zinc fibers, is useful for final mercury cleanup. Wipe down all surrounding areas, as mercury tends to splatter.
- If preferred, the mercury may be sprinkled with zinc metal dust to form an amalgam which is more easily collected than elemental mercury. **WARNING:** *Care must be taken with zinc metal dust, as it expands when damp and may cause a container to explode.*
- If a commercial spill kit is not available:
  - *On a hard surface,* while you're wearing gloves, either use a stiff paper to brush the beads together or use a dropper to collect the beads. **WARNING:** *Do NOT sweep the mercury with a broom, as this creates more vapors and contaminates the broom.* Put all parts—the broken

thermometer, the paper or dropper, and the beads of mercury in a seamless polyethylene or polypropylene bottle or widemouthed jar for regulated disposal. Seal the container and place it in the toxic/caustic waste bin for proper disposal.

- *On a carpet,* the mercury spill should be cut out and disposed of in a toxic/caustic container. **WARNING:** *Do NOT vacuum the mercury because it will cause the mercury to evaporate and become a part of the atmosphere. Incinerating mercury also will cause it to become part of the atmosphere.*
- When you replace mercury thermometers with digital ones, dispose of the mercury thermometers as you would a mercury spill.

## Other Chemical Spills

If a chemical spill occurs in the laboratory or in the classroom, quick action by the teacher can reduce the possibility of injury to a student or the teacher. A chemical spill such as a liter bottle of hydrochloric acid breaking in the chemistry laboratory is considered a major spill.

- Immediately evacuate all students through the exits farthest from the spill. Fumes from a chemical spill can cause severe damage to the body. (See p. 95 for treatment of injuries from chemical spills.)
- Turn on the emergency exhaust fan.
- Contain the spill wearing the proper protective clothing. **WARNING:** *Do NOT allow the spill to trap you.*
- Call for help. The school safety plan should contain the numbers of agencies or departments in your community that will assist in containment and removal of the chemical.

## Biological Spills

Biological spills that occur in a science laboratory or classroom can generate aerosols that can be dispersed in the air throughout the room. These spills can be very dangerous if they involve microorganisms that may be infectious. Any biological material, living or dead, which is a pathogen, or disease-carrying organism, is termed a **biohazard**. The biohazard symbol is universal and should be used on all potential pathogenic material. Any bodily fluids spattered during an accident or as a result of illness should be considered potentially infected. **WARNING:** *Blood spills should be cleaned by persons trained in the task. If an untrained person encounters a blood spill they should limit access to the area and call for assistance immediately.*

- **WARNING:** *AVOID direct skin contact with bodily fluids.*
  - Use disposable gloves when direct hand contact with bodily fluids is necessary.
  - Keep gloves in accessible locations.
  - Wear mask and eye protection or face shield.
  - Wear lab aprons or coats.
  - Remove any contaminated clothing.
  - Vigorously wash the exposed area with soap and water for one minute.
  - Soak up the contents of the spill with paper towels.
- Place contaminated paper towels in a plastic bag for disposal. According to the Centers for Disease Control, infective waste should be either

incinerated or autoclaved before disposal in a sanitary landfill. A school janitor should be familiar with the procedure for your district.

- Sharp items such as needles and scalpel blades should be placed in a red biohazard container made especially for sharp objects.
  - Glassware and microscope slides can be sterilized and reused. See pp. 85.
  - Clean any surface that has been in contact with the fluids with an EPA-approved disinfectant such as a freshly made 1:10 dilution of house-hold bleach.
  - After removing gloves, wash hands for 10 to 15 s with a disinfecting soap and running water.

# Blackline Masters Divider

# Sample Medical Emergency Form

[Name of Teacher]
[Name of School]
[School Address]
[School Phone Number]
*Date form to be returned to teacher:* _____

---------------------------------------------------------------------------------------------------

**Name of Student** _____ **Date of Birth** _____
**Student Address**_____
**Name of Science Class** _____ **Class Period** _____
**Medical Conditions:** _____
_____
_____
_____

**Known Allergies** (include food allergies)**:**
_____
_____
_____

**Medications Taken on a Regular Basis** (include dosage and administering directions)**:**
_____
_____
_____
_____

**Medications Needed for Emergency Allergic Reactions:**
_____
_____
_____

**Person to Call in an Emergency:**
Name: _____ Phone Number (Daytime) _____
Name: _____ Phone Number (Evening) _____
Name: _____ Phone Number (Daytime) _____

Family Doctor: Name_____ Phone Number_____

*In case of an emergency, I hereby authorize the physician selected by school personnel to provide the necessary medical treatment for my child.*

_____
Parent/Guardian (print)

_____
Parent/Guardian (signature)

_____
Date

# Sample Accident Report Form

School _____ Date_____ Time _____

Student's Full Name _____

Student's Address _____

Phone_____ Age _____ Sex _____ Grade _____

*Nature of the Accident*
(select from the following:)

- Abrasion
- Burn
- Puncture or cut
- Ingested material
- Sprain
- Chemical contact
- Other _____

*Region of the Body Injured*
(select from the following:)

- Arm
- Eye
- Head
- Internal
- Leg
- Torso
- Other _____

*Description of the Accident:*

- How the accident occurred

_____

_____

_____

_____

_____

_____

_____

_____

_____

_____

_____

- Location where the accident occurred _____

- List of tools, equipment, or chemicals involved _____

- First aid treatment administered_____

- Who administered first aid? _____

Time parent or guardian notified _____

Student sent: _____ Home _____ Doctor _____ Hospital _____
                                                                     Name of Hospital

_____     _____     _____
        Principal                       Teacher                       Nurse

# Managing Laboratory Work Outside the Classroom

Lab work outside the classroom falls into two categories—home assignments and school-sponsored field trips. Both require thoughtful preparation and planning.

### Home Lab Work

Periodic assignments require students to perform investigations at home. These should not require unusual or expensive materials. You should also provide clear written and verbal instructions. Assume that you as the teacher will be held accountable for materials you might supply the student for the investigations. This pertains to science fair projects as well as course work. See p. 112 for a sample letter to inform parents and guardians of the purpose of home investigation assignments. Note that the letter requests that students conduct the investigations with adult supervision.

### School-Sponsored Field Trips

Field trips provide wonderful opportunities for students to observe and make discoveries about the natural world around them, whether about life, earth, or physical phenomena. Just as in the classroom laboratory, safety is of the utmost importance. This section deals with promoting successful learning opportunities with procedures to lessen the impact of possible dangers. A sample letter to parents, a permission form, and a medical emergency form can be found on pp. 113, 114, and 115.

## Field Trip Administrative Planning Procedures

### Related to School Officials

- Notify and get approval from your school administration.

- Determine the costs of the field trip and how they fit within budget constraints.

- Determine how the timing of the field trip will affect other classes. Notify the teachers involved.

- Determine whether substitute teacher(s) will be needed.

- Verify that the field trip relates to and augments your course of study. Will it also augment other courses?

- Confirm whether there are school regulations that would restrict some students, such as those with discipline problems, from attending the field trip. What arrangements will need to be made for those students on the day of the field trip?

- Determine the length of time you need at the site for the activities you have planned. Allow time for relaxation in your plan. Also allow time for cleanup.

- Determine the number of sponsors you need for the number of students who will attend.

- Identify and recruit the number of sponsors you need. Ask parents or guardians to lend their expertise.

- Make a list of students who are going and leave it with their permissions forms with a school official.

Field Work

- Make arrangements for taking investigation materials (magnifying glasses, test tubes, and so forth) with you.

- Make arrangements for taking personal safety equipment (goggles, gloves, and aprons) with you.

## Related to the Field Site

- Visit the site ahead of time to be sure it is appropriate for your needs.

- **WARNING:** *Consider health concerns of your students that might be aggravated by conditions at the site.* Verify that the site can accommodate students on crutches or in wheel chairs.

- Find out who must authorize the field work at the site. Obtain permission from the proper officials.

- Find out the requirements you and your students must meet to gain permission to visit the site. Determine how these requirements will affect your plans.

- Find out whether the site charges admission fees and if so, how much they are.

- Pick an alternate site in case there are too many obstacles to using the original site.

- Set a date for the field trip. Select an alternate date in case of inclement weather.

- Check to see whether guides or forest rangers will be required.

- Determine what kind of restroom and lunch shelters/facilities are available. Will students need to bring their own lunches?

- Verify the location of a first aid station or other emergency services.

## Related to Students and Parents

- Decide whether you need to have a meeting with the parents.

- Write a letter to parents and guardians regarding the purpose of the field work. (See p. 113 for sample letter.)

- Make clear to parents and guardians what you expect of the students.

- Inform the parents and guardians what costs are to be shared by them and the students.

- Inform parents of your contingency plans should unexpected bad weather occur.

- Send home a permissions form with a date by which it must be returned. (See p. 114)

- Send home a medical emergency form with a date by which it must be returned. (See p. 115)

### Regarding Transportation

- Determine which type of transportation is reliable and available.

- Confirm the cost of transportation and how it is to be paid—school or students—or plan another way to raise money to pay for the transportation.

- Determine the length of travel time, including loading and unloading.

- Provide parents with details regarding transportation.

- Determine whether additional insurance is needed for field trips.

- Make a contingency plan in case a vehicle breaks down.

- Find out whether transportation permission forms are needed.

- Make sure there will be fire safety equipment on board the vehicle(s).

- Make sure there will be a well-stocked first aid kit available. (See p. 141.)

## Preparing Students for Field Trips

- Verify that students have the background necessary to be successful in the planned field work.

- Plan activities that will engage students actively in learning.

- Inform students of the purpose of the field work.

- Establish how you expect students to behave and inform them of the consequences of unsafe actions.

- Give students the parental letter and necessary permission forms to take home and make clear the due date for the forms to be returned.

- Instruct students regarding dangerous plants or animals they might encounter. Present visuals to help them recognize these.

- Inform students of the type of clothing they should wear.

- Notify students regarding needs for insect repellant and sunscreen.

- Inform students if they need to bring their own lunch and drinking water.

- Make research assignments to help students gain background for the planned activities.

## On-Site Supervision

- Take mobile phones in case of emergency.

- Make sure well-stocked first aid kits are readily available.

- Take students' medical emergency forms with you.

- Follow school and local regulations regarding the handling of students' medication—prescriptions and over-the-counter medicines recommended by physicians—that students may need for medical conditions and for emergency allergic reactions.

- Designate study teams and safety partners.

- Inform students who the supervisors/sponsors are and where they will be.

- Assign specific tasks to the sponsors.

- Make clear the boundaries within which the students must stay.

- Clearly inform students of what is expected of them, in conduct and in the outcomes of their observations and investigations. Make clear the timetable and signal for returning to a pre-selected spot.

- Make clear how the field work will be evaluated.

- Distribute materials needed for the investigation (magnifying glasses, test tubes, and so forth).

- Provide students with goggles, gloves, and aprons.

- Inform students to notify you or a sponsor *immediately* in case of an emergency. Establish evacuation or other necessary procedures.

- **WARNING:** *Some substances, while harmless to many, may pose serious reactions in others. Be prepared to deal with these.*

- **WARNING:** *Inform students NOT to eat berries or other vegetation or food items they come upon and to use gloves when handling items they are investigating.*

- **WARNING:** *Inform students of the need to change clothing and wash with soap and water after the field work to lessen the chance of irritation from their exposure to plant and wildlife.*

## Dealing with Emergencies

### Accidents in the Field

- If the accident is serious, administer first aid while someone else calls for emergency services. Notify the parents or guardians. (See pp. 94–97 for basic first-aid procedures.)

- If the accident is not serious, administer first aid and then notify parents or guardians.

- When you return to school or at an appropriate time, file an accident report. (See p. 116 for a sample form.)

### Weather Emergencies
*Flash Floods*

- **WARNING:** *Get to higher ground if rising water is threatening.*

- **WARNING:** *Do NOT drive through flooded intersections or stretches of road. AVOID small rivers or streams, canyons, and dry riverbeds.*

- **WARNING:** *Do NOT try to walk through flowing water more than an ankle deep.*

- **WARNING:** *Keep students away from drainage ditches, viaducts, storm drains, and other flooded area.*

### Tornado Conditions

- **WARNING:** *If possible, go to a basement or interior room at ground level.*

- **WARNING:** *AVOID large expanses of glass.*

- **WARNING:** *Move from large open areas such as cafeterias, gymnasiums, and auditoriums, but stay indoors.*

- **WARNING:** *Crouch down and cover your head with your hands and with coats, blankets, or pillows if they are available.*

- **WARNING:** *Leave motor vehicles and find other shelter.*

- **WARNING:** *If shelter is not available, lie down in a low area and cover your head with your hands.*

- **WARNING:** *Do NOT seek shelter under an overpass. Wind tunnel conditions can occur.*

### Lightning Conditions

- **WARNING:** *If you are outdoors, find safe shelter immediately. A hardtop car or a bus with the windows up offers protection if you cannot find a building.*

- **WARNING:** *If you are in a* boat *or are* swimming, *seek shelter immediately away from the water.*

- **WARNING:** *If you are in a* wooded area, *crouch down under a thick growth of the smallest trees.*

- **WARNING:** *If you feel your hair standing on end, squat down with your head between your knees. Do NOT lie down.*

- **WARNING:** *AVOID tall, isolated objects, including trees; bodies of water; fences; open doorways and windows; and open vehicles.*

## Accidents Involving Transportation

- Call emergency numbers immediately and administer first aid. (See pp. 94–97 for some basic first aid procedures.)

- Follow local regulations regarding accidents with vehicles.

- File necessary reports with the police or fire departments.

- When you have returned to school, file the appropriate accident report with your school administration. (See p. 116.)

## Blackline Masters Divider

# Sample Parental Letter Regarding Home Lab Work

[date]

Dear Parent or Guardian:

Periodically your child/ward will be assigned lab activities to be conducted at home. These activities have been tested by teachers and deemed appropriate for independent completion. It is, however, recommended that an adult supervise or participate with the child to be certain that all safety precautions are being followed. The activities have been designed to use ordinary items found in the home.

If you have any concerns regarding the materials suggested or the advisability of your child/ward conducting the lab activities, please don't hesitate to call me at school between [hour] and [hour].

Sincerely,

[Teacher signature]
[Teacher name, printed]
[School name]
[School address]
[School phone number]

# Sample Parental Letter Regarding Field Trips

[Teacher Name]
[School Name]
[School Address]
[School Phone Number]

Dear Parent or Guardian:

A field trip is planned for [date] for science classes from [school name]. The [duration of trip] to [name of site] will be to study [purpose of study]. Students will observe and investigate such natural events and features as [list sample topics].

Departure time is approximately [time] at [location of departure (where students need to be taken if before usual school arrival time)]. Return time is approximately [time] at [location (if later than usual school dismissal time)]. Transportation will be provided by [type of transportation]. Travel time is estimated at [duration] to and from the site.

Lunch will [be provided at the site for a cost of $0.00/need to be brought by students as well as water or other beverage to drink].

Students should wear [type of clothing and shoes]. Please provide sunscreen and insect repellant for your child/ward. Investigation materials and safety equipment will be provided by the school.

Adult sponsors will accompany me to provide additional instruction and supervision. Students will be required to meet all verbal and written instructions regarding their lab work and their behavior.

Please read and sign the attached Permission Form and the Emergency Medical Form and return to me no later than [date]. Please send any needed medications with your child on the day of the field trip. I will carry the medication until needed. In an emergency, you may reach us by cell phone at [insert number]. In case the cell phone is out-of-range, the phone number at the site is [phone number] and the contact person there is [name].

We are very pleased about this opportunity for discovering interesting features of our world. If you have any questions regarding this field trip, don't hesitate to call me at school between [hour] and [hour].

Sincerely,



[Teacher's signature]
[Teacher's name, printed]

# Sample Permission Form for Field Trips

[date]

After reading the letter informing me of the details of the field trip planned for [date] _____ to [name of site], I hereby:

❏ Give permission
❏ Deny permission

for my child/ward _____ to participate in the activity.
This permission extends to traveling via [form of transportation named in the letter]. I understand the time of departure is scheduled for _____.
I agree to pick up my child/ward at [the time of arrival](if it is after normal school closing) at [location at school].

_____
Parent/Guardian (print name)

_____
Parent/Guardian (signature)

_____
Date

Return this form to [name of teacher] no later than [date].

[School Name]
[School Address]
[School Phone Number]

# Sample Medical Emergency Form

[Name of Teacher]
[Name of School]
[School Address]
[School Phone Number]
*Date form to be returned to teacher:*_____

----------------------------------------------------------------------------------

**Name of Student** _____ **Date of Birth** _____
**Student Address**_____
**Name of Science Class** _____ **Class Period** _____
**Medical Conditions:** _____
_____
_____
_____

**Known Allergies** (include food allergies)**:**
_____
_____
_____

**Medications Taken on a Regular Basis** (include dosage and administering directions)**:**
_____
_____
_____
_____

**Medications Needed for Emergency Allergic Reactions:**
_____
_____
_____

**Person to Call in an Emergency:**
Name: _____  Phone Number (Daytime) _____
Name: _____  Phone Number (Evening) _____
Name: _____  Phone Number (Daytime) _____

Family Doctor: Name_____  Phone Number_____

*In case of an emergency, I hereby authorize the physician selected by school personnel to provide the necessary medical treatment for my child.*

_____
Parent/Guardian (print)

_____
Parent/Guardian (signature)

_____
Date

# Sample Accident Report Form

School _____ Date_____ Time _____

Student's Full Name _____

Student's Address _____

Phone_____ Age _____ Sex _____ Grade _____

*Nature of the Accident*
(select from the following:)

- Abrasion
- Burn
- Puncture or cut
- Ingested material
- Sprain
- Chemical contact
- Other _____

*Region of the Body Injured*
(select from the following:)

- Arm
- Eye
- Head
- Internal
- Leg
- Torso
- Other _____

*Description of the Accident:*

- How the accident occurred

_____

_____

_____

_____

_____

_____

_____

_____

_____

_____

_____

- Location where the accident occurred _____

- List of tools, equipment, or chemicals involved _____

- First aid treatment administered_____

- Who administered first aid? _____

Time parent or guardian notified _____

Student sent: _____ Home _____ Doctor _____ Hospital _____
                                                      Name of Hospital

_____          _____          _____
         Principal                          Teacher                            Nurse

# Managing Laboratory Materials Storage

It is your responsibility to be informed of the rules—local, state, federal, and school—governing storage and disposal of materials used in your classroom/laboratory. This section discusses Material Safety Data Sheets, inventory practices, storage factors such as the nature of hazardous materials and chemical incompatibility, storage and handling procedures, and waste disposal. Refer to pp. 133–136 regarding factors involved in the construction of storeroom facilities.

## Material Safety Data Sheets (MSDS)

You should keep an MSDS file for all the chemicals you use and store in your classroom/laboratory. Manufacturers provide a MSDS for each chemical they produce. An MSDS includes the following and more:

- The name of the chemical

- Manufacturer's name and address

- Physical and health hazards including organs it would affect

- First aid measures

- CAS number assigned by the Chemical Abstract Service

- Chemical formula

- Molecular weight for compounds, the atomic weight for elements

- Common name of the chemical

- Purity of the substance

- Lot numbers

- Supplier's name and address

See pp. 118–121 for a sample MSDS. Note that the sample is for sodium chloride (salt), a common substance not considered hazardous. Even so, there are several safety issues concerning salt (indicated by the highlighted portions of the MSDS).

Material Storage

# MATERIAL SAFETY DATA SHEET

*Sodium Chloride 25%*

90175

## SECTION 1—CHEMICAL PRODUCT AND COMPANY IDENTIFICATION

*MSDS Name:* Sodium Chloride 25%
*Catalog Numbers:* 99150
*Synonyms:* None
*Company Identification:* [Manufacturer's name and address go here]
*For information, call:* [Manufacturer's phone numbers]
*Emergency Number:*
For CHEMTREC assistance, call:
For International CHEMTREC assistance, call:

## SECTION 2—COMPOSITION, INFORMATION ON INGREDIENTS

| CAS# | Chemical Name | % | EINECS# |
|------|---------------|---|---------|
| 7647-14-5 | Sodium Chloride | 25% | 231-598-3 |
| 7732-18-5 | Water | 75% | 231-791-2 |

## SECTION 3—HAZARDS IDENTIFICATION

EMERGENCY OVERVIEW

*Appearance*: colorless

**CAUTION!** May cause respiratory tract irritation. May cause eye and skin irritation. May cause digestive tract irritation with nausea, vomiting, and diarrhea.

*Target Organs:* none

*Potential Health Effects*

   *Eye:* May cause eye irritation.

   *Skin:* May cause skin irritation.

   *Ingestion:* Ingestion of large amounts may cause gastrointestinal irritation. Ingestion of large amounts may cause nausea and vomiting, rigidity or convulsions. Continued exposure can produce coma, dehydration, and internal organ congestion.

   *Inhalation*: May cause respiratory tract irritation

   *Chronic:* No information found

## SECTION 4—FIRST AID MEASURES

*Eyes:* Flush eyes with plenty of water for at least 15 minutes, occasionally lifting the upper and lower lids. If irritation develops, get medical aid.

*Skin:* Get medical aid if irritation develops or persists. Flush skin with plenty of soap and water.

*Ingestion*: If victim is conscious and alert, give 2 to 4 cupfuls of milk or water. Never give anything by mouth to an unconscious person. Get medical aid if irritation or symptoms occur.

*Inhalation*: Remove from exposure to fresh air immediately. If not breathing, give artificial respiration. If breathing is difficult, give oxygen. Get medical aid if cough or other symptoms appear.

*Notes to Physician:* None

*Antidote:* None reported

## SECTION 5—FIRE FIGHTING MEASURES

*General Information:* As in any fire, wear a self-contained breathing apparatus in pressure-demand, MSHA/NIOSH (approved or equivalent), and full protective gear.

*Extinguishing Media:* For small fires, use water spray, dry chemical, carbon dioxide or chemical foam.

   *Auto-ignition*: Temperature: Not available

   *Flash Point*: Not available

   *NFPA Rating:* Not published

   *Explosion Limits, Lower*: Not available

   *Upper:* Not available

## SECTION 6—ACCIDENTAL RELEASE MEASURES

*General Information*: Use proper personal protective equipment as indicated in Section 8.
*Spills/Leaks*: Flush spill area with water.

## SECTION 7—HANDLING and STORAGE

*Handling*: Wash thoroughly after handling. Use with adequate ventilation. Avoid contact with skin and eyes. Avoid ingestion and inhalation.
*Storage*: Store in a cool, dry place. Store in a tightly closed container.

## SECTION 8—EXPOSURE CONTROLS, PERSONAL PROTECTION

*Engineering Controls:* Good general ventilation should be sufficient to control airborne levels.

Exposure Limits

| Chemical Name | ACGIH | NIOSH | OSHA—Final PELs |
| --- | --- | --- | --- |
| Sodium Chloride | None listed | None listed | None listed |
| Water | None listed | None listed | None listed |

*OSHA Vacated PELs:*
Sodium chloride: No OSHA Vacated PELs are listed for this chemical.
Water: No OSHA Vacated PELs are listed for this chemical.
Personal Protective Equipment
*Eyes:* Wear appropriate protective eyeglasses or chemical safety goggles as described by OSHA's eye and face protection regulations in 29 CFR 1910.133 or European Standard EN166.
*Skin:* Wear appropriate gloves to prevent skin exposure.
*Clothing:* Wear appropriate protective clothing to minimize contact with skin.
*Respirators:* Follow the OSHA respirator regulations found in 29 CFR 1910.134 or European Standard EN 149. Always use a NIOSH or European Standard EN 149 approved respirator when necessary.

## SECTION 9—PHYSICAL AND CHEMICAL PROPERTIES

*Physical State:* Solid
*Appearance:* colorless
*Odor:* Odorless
*pH:* Not available
*Vapor Pressure:* Not available
*Vapor Density:* Not available
*Evaporation Rate:* Not available
*Viscosity:* Not available
*Boiling Point:* Not available
*Freezing/Melting Point:* Not available
*Decomposition Temperature:* Not available
*Solubility:* Soluble in water
*Specific Gravity/Density:* Not available
*Molecular Formula:* Solution
*Molecular Weight:* Not available

## SECTION 10—STABILITY AND REACTIVITY

*Chemical Stability:* Stable
*Conditions to Avoid:* High temperatures
*Incompatibilities with Other Materials:* Reacts with most non-noble metals such as iron or steel, building materials (such as cement), bromine, or trifluoride. Potentially explosive reaction with dichloromaleic anhydride + urea. Electrolysis of mixtures with nitrogen compounds may form explosive nitrogen trichloride.
*Hazardous Decomposition Products:* Chlorine, toxic fumes of sodium oxide.
*Hazardous Polymerization:* Has not been reported.

## SECTION 11—TOXICOLOGICAL INFORMATION

*RTECS#:*
   CAS# 7647-14-5: VZ4725000
   CAS# 7732-18-5: ZC0110000
*LD50/LC50:*
   CAS# 7647-14-5: Oral, mouse: LD50 = 4 gm/kg; Oral, rat: LD50 = 3 gm/kg.
   CAS# 7732-18-5: Oral, rat: LD50 = >90 mL/kg.
*Carcinogenicity:* Sodium chloride—Not listed by ACGIH, IARC, NIOSH, NTP, or OSHA.
      Water—Not listed by ACGIH, IARC, NIOSH, NTP, or OSHA.
*Epidemiology:* No information reported
*Teratogenicity:* An experimental teratogen
*Reproductive Effects:* Human reproductive effects by intraplacental route: Terminates pregnancy;
Experimental reproductive effects
*Neurotoxicity:* No information reported
*Mutagenicity:* Human mutation data reported
*Other Studies:* No information reported

## SECTION 12—ECOLOGICAL INFORMATION

*Ecotoxicity:* No information found
*Environmental Fate:* No information reported
*Physical/Chemical:* No information found
*Other:* No information found

## SECTION 13—DISPOSAL CONSIDERATIONS

Dispose of in a manner consistent with federal, state, and local regulations.
RCRA D-Series Maximum Concentration of Contaminants: None listed
RCRA D-Series Chronic Toxicity Reference Levels: None listed
RCRA F-Series: None listed
RCRA P-Series: None listed
RCRA U-Series: None listed
Not listed as a material banned from land disposal according to RCRA.

## SECTION 14—TRANSPORT INFORMATION

*US DOT:* No information available
*IMO:* No information available
*IATA*: No information available
*RID/ADR:* No information available
*Canadian TDG*: No information available

## SECTION 15—REGULATORY INFORMATION

<u>US FEDERAL</u>
*TSCA:*
   CAS# 7647-14-5 is listed on the TSCA inventory.
   CAS# 7732-18-5 is listed on the TSCA inventory.
*Health & Safety Reporting List:*
   None of the chemicals are on the Health & Safety Reporting List.
*Chemical Test Rules:*
   None of the chemicals in this product are under a Chemical Test Rule.
Section 12b:
   None of the chemicals is listed under TSCA Section 12b.
*TSCA Significant New Use Rule:*
   None of the chemicals in this material has a SNUR under TSCA.
*SARA:*
*Section 302 (RQ):* None of the chemicals in this material has an RQ.
*Section 302 (TPQ):* None of the chemicals in this product has a TPQ.

*SARA Codes*
    CAS # 7647-14-5: acute
    Section 313: No chemicals are reportable under Section 313.
*Clean Air Act:*
    This material does not contain any hazardous air pollutants.
    This material does not contain any Class 1 Ozone depletors.
    This material does not contain any Class 2 Ozone depletors.
*Clean Water Act:*
    None of the chemicals in this product is listed as Hazardous.
*Substances under the CWA:* None of the chemicals in this product is listed as Priority.
*Pollutants under the CWA:* None of the chemicals in this product is listed as a Toxic *Pollutant under the CWA.*
<u>OSHA:</u>
    None of the chemicals in this product is considered highly hazardous by OSHA.
<u>STATE</u>
    Sodium chloride is not present on state lists from CA, PA, MN, MA, FL, or NJ.
    Water is not present on state lists from CA, PA, MN, MA, FL, or NJ.
    California: No Significant Risk Level; None of the chemicals in this product is listed.
<u>*European/International Regulations*</u>
European Labeling in Accordance with EC Directives
    Hazard Symbols: Not available
    Risk Phrases:
    Safety Phrases:
<u>*WGK (Water Danger/Protection)*</u>
    CAS# 7647-14-5: 0
    CAS# 7732-18-5: No information available
<u>*Canada*</u>
    CAS# 7647-14-5 is listed on Canada's DSL/NDSL List.
    CAS# 7732-18-5 is listed on Canada's DSL/NDSL List.
    *WHMIS:* Not available
    CAS# 7647-14-5 is not listed on Canada's Ingredient Disclosure List.
    CAS# 7732-18-5 is not listed on Canada's Ingredient Disclosure List.
Exposure Limits

## SECTION 16—ADDITIONAL INFORMATION

*MSDS Creation Date:* 5/14/1996
*Revision #1 Date:* 9/02/1997

The information above is believed to be accurate and represents the best information currently available to us. However, we make no warranty of merchantability or any other warranty, express or implied, with respect to such information, and we assume no liability resulting from its use. Users should make their own investigations to determine the suitability of the information for their particular purposes. In no way shall [the manufacturer] be liable for any claims, losses, or damages of any third party or for lost profits or any special, indirect, incidental, consequential or exemplary damages, howsoever arising, even if [the manufacturer] has been advised of the possibility of such damages.

# Inventory Practices

- All items in your classroom/laboratory should be labeled with the name of the substance, its source, acquisition and/or expiration date, whether it is hazardous, and necessary first aid steps. Chemicals should have chemical formula and concentration listed.

- A computer inventory program can simplify the process of finding a substance if you have a computer located near the storeroom. An alphabetized printout, manual listing, or file card system also works well. Information should include all items on the label plus the type of substance (chemical, biological, radioactive, and so forth), condition, amount, size of container, and location in the storage room.

- Conduct periodic (at least once a year) inspections and cleanup efforts. For reasons of personal safety, two persons (NOT students) should be involved. Safety devices, such as goggles, masks, aprons, and gloves should be worn. The storeroom should be well ventilated (see p. 136).

- Check stored substances for signs of leakage, deterioration, loose labels, or other problems.

- Control the amount of substances you have on hand. Check regulations for your area to find out what the legal limit is.

- Reduce your inventory by reordering only those substances needed in the following year or so, using small-scale chemistry amounts if possible (see p. 137).

- Take steps to dispose of all outdated, contaminated, and unlabeled materials (see pp. 129–130).

- Also dispose of those substances that have not been used in the last year or two as well as hazardous materials that should not be used in a classroom/laboratory.

- If possible, purchase materials by school or school district to prevent duplication and to buy in bulk for lower prices. **WARNING:** *Substances purchased in bulk and then transferred to smaller containers for individual schools MUST be labeled properly and placed into proper containers. Follow all safety regulations in the transfer of the substances.*

# Storage Factors

Factors that affect how you store materials in your storeroom include the properties of hazardous materials, patterns to storeroom organization, and proper procedures for storing and handling various materials. Many computer software programs are available with contain chemical storage patterns. You may wish to code each shelf area by group or type of substance. Mark that code on the label of the substance with a waterproof marker to help ensure that the substance is returned to the correct shelf after use. Also enter the code in your inventory record. **WARNING:** *Do NOT return unused substances to the original container. Contamination may cause unwanted reactions.*

## The Nature of Hazardous Materials

Follow regulations for storing hazardous materials (check your MSDS file). Follow all precautions when handling hazardous materials. Note that some materials may pose more then one type of hazard. Types of hazardous materials include:

*Corrosives* Corrosives are materials that can injure body tissues or are damaging to metal by direct chemical reaction.

- Examples of corrosive acids are sulfuric, acetic, hydrochloric, and nitric acids.
- Examples of corrosive bases are caustic soda and aqueous ammonia. Caustic refers to a base that is corrosive. For example, caustic soda is solid crystals of sodium hydroxide.
- Other corrosive substances include iodine, bromine, anhydride, and ferric chloride.

*Flammable Liquids and Solids* Liquids usually do not burn but produce vapors that do. Examples are solvents such as acetone, ethanol, toluene, and glacial acetic acid. **WARNING:** *Vapors from flammable solids are as dangerous as from liquids.*

## Toxic Substances

- enter the body by ingestion, skin contact, or inhalation.
- *Acute effects* occur suddenly or within a few hours. For example, methyl alcohol can cause blindness or death if even small amounts are swallowed or inhaled.
- *Chronic effects* result from repeated exposure over months or years and are dose dependent—calling for using the smallest amounts possible and following all precautions. Examples are benzene and formaldehyde.

*Oxidizers and Reactives* These are chemicals that can explode, violently polymerize, form explosive peroxides, or are pyrophoric. Pyrophoric substances may ignite spontaneously when exposed to water or oxygen.

- Examples of oxidizers include nitric acid, hydrogen peroxide, potassium nitrate and nitrite.
- Examples of substances that form hazardous polymers upon aging include acrylonitrile and butadiene.
- Examples of substances that can form, within a few months, explosive peroxides include aldehydes, ethers, ketones, and vinyl compounds.
- Examples of pyrophoric substances include calcium carbide, sodium, and magnesium powder.

### Pathogens

- **WARNING:** *All human, animal, and plant specimens present a potential hazard from pathogens.*
- Be selective in choosing microorganisms for laboratory activities. Reputable suppliers will list known or suspected pathogens in their catalogs.
- Purchase biological specimens in preservatives with low toxicity. Formaldehyde or formalin are no longer recommended as preservatives. Obtain an MSDS from suppliers for their holding and shipping fluid. Ethylene glycol is a significant ingredient in most nonformaldehyde preservative preparations. **WARNING:** *Etylene glycol is toxic when ingested, even in small amounts. Use precautions. Thorough rinsing of specimens, wearing gloves, and good ventilation are required.*

**Radioactive Materials** Radiation naturally occurs in uranium ores. Uranium ores are largely unregulated; however, this does NOT make them safe. Overexposure to radiation can cause burns and cancer. Ores should be evaluated before use. They should not subject an individual to radiation levels of more than 5 millirems during an hour.

## Chemical Compatibility

A major factor in storing and handling chemicals is knowing which chemicals work with other chemicals. For example, carbon tetrachloride and chloroform have been widely used in the past as nonpolar solutes. Because of health concerns, substitutes are now being used. However, acetone is NOT a suitable replacement for them. Acetone is miscible with water and many organic solvents. Many nonpolar solutes will not dissolve in acetone. Instead, petroleum ether, which is a mixture of alkanes similar to gasoline, are often used as substitutes for tetrachloride and chloroform.

Safety also is a factor regarding chemicals that are incompatible. See pp. 125 and 126 for a reference sheet listing several examples of incompatible chemicals.

# Chemical Incompatibility Reference Sheet

| Chemical | | Not compatible with |
|---|---|---|
| **Gases** | Acetylene | Bromine, chlorine, copper, fluorine, mercury, silver |
| | Ammonia (anhydrous) | Bromine, calcium hypochlorite, chlorine, iodine, mercury<br>**WARNING:** *This chemical is deadly by itself.* |
| | Hydrocarbons (such as butane and propane) | Bromine, chlorine, chromic acid, fluorine, sodium peroxide |
| | Hydrogen sulfide | Fuming nitric acid, oxidizing gases<br>**WARNING:** *This chemical is deadly by itself.* |
| | Oxygen | Oils; grease; hydrogen; flammable liquids, solids, or gases |
| **Liquids** | Acetic acid | Ammonium nitrate, chromic acid, ethylene glycol, hydroxyl compounds, nitric acid, perchloric acid, permanganates, peroxides |
| | Acetic anhydride | Water |
| | Acetone | Concentrated nitric and sulfuric acid mixtures |
| | Aniline | Hydrogen peroxide, nitric acid |
| | Flammable liquids | Ammonium nitrate, chromic acid, halogens, hydrogen peroxide, nitric acid, sodium peroxide |
| | Hydrogen peroxide (6% or more) | Acetone, alcohols, aniline, chromium, combustible materials, copper, iron and iron oxides, most metals and their salts, organic materials |
| | Mercury | Acetylene, ammonia |
| | Nitric acid (concentrated) | Acetic acid, alcohol, aniline, brass, copper, flammable gases and liquids, heavy metals, hydrogen sulfide, phosphorus |
| | Oxalic acid | Mercury, silver |
| | Sulfides | Acids |
| | Sulfuric acid | Carbohydates, most metals, potassium chlorate, potassium perchlorate, potassium permanganate and other similar compounds of light metals such as sodium or lithium, reducing agents |
| | Toluene | Strong acids, strong oxidizing agents |

# Chemical Incompatibility
# Reference Sheet (continued)

| Chemical | | Not compatible with |
|---|---|---|
| **Solids** | Alkali and alkaline Earth metals (powdered Al or Mg, Ca, Li, Na, K) | Carbon dioxide, chlorinated hydrocarbons, halogens, water |
| | Aluminum metal | Ammonium nitrate; antimony trichloride; bromine vapor; any bromate, chlorate, or iodate |
| | Ammonium nitrate | Acids, chlorates, flammable liquids, nitrites, powdered metals, sulfur, finely divided organic or combustible materials |
| | Calcium oxide | Water |
| | Carbon (activated) | Calcium hypochlorite, all oxidizing agents |
| | Chlorates | Acids, ammonium salts, powdered metals, sulfur, finely divided organic or combustible materials, reducing agents |
| | Copper | Acetylene, hydrogen peroxide |
| | Cyanides | Acids<br>**WARNING:** *This chemical is deadly by itself.* |
| | Iodine | Acetylene, ammonia, hydrogen |
| | Nitrates | Reducing agents, sulfuric acid |
| | Nitrites | Acids |
| | Potassium | Carbon dioxide, water |
| | Potassium permanganate | Ethylene glycol, glycerol, sulfuric acid |
| | Selenides | Acids, reducing agents |
| | Silver | Acetylene, ammonium compounds, oxalic acid, tartaric acid |
| | Sodium | Carbon dioxide, sulfur, water |
| | Sodium nitrate | Ammonium nitrate and other ammonium salts |
| | Sodium peroxide | Acetic anhydride, carbon disulfide, ethylene glycol, ethyl acetate, ethyl or methyl alcohol, glacial acetic acid, glycerin, methyl acetate |

# Storage Procedures

The procedures that follow pertain to all areas, including *earthquake-prone areas*. For additional information, suppliers describe storage patterns in their catalogs.

## General Storage Patterns and Procedures

- Students should NOT have access to the storeroom area.
- **WARNING:** *Do NOT store hazardous substances above eye level and NEVER on the floor.*
- Larger equipment and larger chemical containers should be stored on lower shelves only.
- **WARNING:** *Do NOT store materials in direct sunlight.*
- Substances should be stored at the correct temperature.
- Storeroom temperature should be monitored on a regular basis.
- All storage shelves and cabinets should be securely attached to the walls. **WARNING:** *Do NOT place hazardous materials in unstable containers or in an apparatus that is not properly secured.*
- Samples of asbestos should be kept in clear, unbreakable containers that resist opening. **WARNING:** *Asbestos is a known carcinogen and all must be protected from asbestos dust or fibers.*
- Poisons should be kept locked in a cabinet.
- Keep all containers of biological specimens in locked storage.
- Keep all syringes and scalpel blades in locked storage.

## Handling Radioactive Materials

- Follow all regulations regarding the handling of radioactive materials. All sources should be shielded, handled, and transported in a manner to prevent anyone from being exposed to unnecessary radiation. Normally, "Caution: Radiation Area" signs are posted when radioactive materials are present. However, NO school should have enough radioactive material (5 millirems) to warrant such a sign.
- **WARNING:** *Dinosaur bones may be radioactive and should NOT be in a classroom laboratory unless they test at safe levels of radioactivity.* Dinosaur bones should be kept in sealed containers and washed off before being handled (with gloves).

## Storing Chemicals

- Store only those chemicals you intend to use.
- Store chemicals in a separate dedicated room different from the preparation/equipment storeroom.
- Allow sufficient room to store chemicals according to compatible chemical families A partial list of incompatible reagents can be found on pp. 125 and 126.
- Separate chemicals by reaction type. Store acids in one place and bases in another. Oxidants should be stored away from easily oxidized materials.
- Peroxide production in aldehydes, ethers, ketones, and vinyl compounds can be slowed by storing them in full containers, by closing containers as soon as possible, and by tightly closing the containers' lids or caps, which limits exposure to oxygen.
- Store pyrophorics with a layer of mineral oil or kerosene over them to prevent contact with the air.

- Store any source of ignition separately from other ignition sources or combustible materials. Ignition sources include sparkers, strikers, lighters, matches, lenses, and parabolic mirrors.
- Water-reactive chemicals (metals) should be stored where they will remain dry.
- Chemicals should be stored in an upright position and be placed no more than two containers deep.
- **WARNING:** *Chemicals should NOT be stored in fume hoods.*
- Refrigeration may be required to minimize decomposition or volatility. Use only spark-free refrigeration in laboratories, storage rooms, and preparation areas for storage of flammable chemicals (see p. 142). **WARNING**: *Do NOT use laboratory refrigerators for the storage of edibles.*
- Acids and corrosives should be stored in a nonmetal or coated metal, vented cabinet. The acid cabinet should be vented to the outside to prevent a buildup of toxic fumes. (See p. 136.) A separate nitric acid compartment or cabinet must be provided to separate nitric acid from the other inorganic acids or readily oxidized substances.
- Store flammable reagents in the smallest quantities possible. Store flammable liquids in appropriate safety cabinets and/or safety cans. WARNING: *Do NOT store flammables in a household-type refrigerator. Instead, use an explosion-proof refrigerator. (See p. 142.)*
- Chemical shelving should have restraints to contain the chemicals. One- to two-inch wooden edge lips are acceptable, or stretch cords or 1/8-inch stainless steel rods can be anchored to the individual shelves and set about two inches above shelf level. **WARNING:** *Use caution when removing containers from shelves with lips so that they do not catch on the lip and tip over and spill.*

## Handling Live Animals

- All live animals should be treated with care and respect.
- Animals require specific diets and living conditions. Be sure to check with reliable sources about these requirements.
- Animals need full time care so arrangements must be made for weekends and holidays.
- Mammals should be vaccinated for rabies.
- Any pet brought to class should have a clean bill of health from a veterinarian.
- Contact special events directors regarding the use and handling of animals in science fairs and other research projects.

# Waste Disposal Policies

This section discusses issues involved in waste generated from wholesale cleanup of a laboratory and storage room and possible methods of disposal to include in your policies and waste disposal plans. Refer to pp. 83–85 regarding daily cleanup and temporary waste disposal. **WARNING**: *If you store non-hazardous wastes with hazardous wastes, the entire content of the storage MUST be considered hazardous waste.*

## Reducing Waste

An important step in managing waste disposal is finding ways to reduce the amount of waste you generate. Reducing the amount of waste generated reduces the costs of waste disposal and fosters a safer environment in the science laboratory. Consider the following:

- Buy only the amount of chemicals needed within the next one to two years at the most.
- Scale down the amount of chemicals you use in each activity. Most macroscale experiments can be scaled down by up to 50 percent with little effort or change in equipment. Refer to the section on small-scale chemistry on p. 37 for more information about reducing the amounts of chemicals even more.
- Many chemistry labs contain chemicals that were purchased in bulk years ago and that either have gone bad or are no longer needed. Any initial savings will therefore be thrown away. Costs of waste disposal increase when it involves old and unstable materials.
- Students should NOT be working with hazardous chemicals, and it is expensive to dispose of them as regulated waste. When you discontinue use of the hazardous chemical, any amount remaining in the inventory will require legal disposal as a hazardous waste. Be sure not to order more. Substitute non- or less-hazardous chemicals for hazardous chemicals within experiments.
- Use alcohol or hexane thermometers in place of mercury thermometers if close accuracy is unnecessary.
- Use cyclohexane in place of benzene in molecular weight determination/freezing point experiments.
- Store biological specimens in isopropyl alcohol, sodium citrate, or other safer preservative in place of formaldehyde.
- Use cyclohexane in place of carbon tetrachloride in halide ion tests.
- A 40 percent glyoxal solution may be substituted for formalin (a 40 percent formaldehyde solution) in some demonstrations.

## Chemical Disposal

Local, state, and federal laws regulate the disposal of chemicals. Consult these laws before attempting to dispose of any chemicals.

- Prior to chemical disposal, identify which chemicals need to be disposed of. These include:
  - out-of-date or contaminated chemicals.
  - chemicals without legible labels.
  - chemicals that are too hazardous for student use.

- **WARNING:** *Some substances should NOT be removed from storage except by certified teachers. Some of these include benzoyl peroxide, carbon disulfide, diisopropyl ether, ethyl ether, perchloric acid, and potassium metal.* NOTE: *Picric acid is outlawed for school use—if any is found in a school lab, trained officials must be called.*
- Store wastes in tightly closed, compatible containers. For example, do not store acid waste in metal containers.
  - **WARNING:** *Do NOT mix organic and inorganic wastes.*
  - **WARNING**: *Do NOT mix halogenated and non-halogenated solvents.*

**Where to Dispose of Chemicals** Federal, state, and local laws regulate the amount and kinds of chemicals that may be put in a landfill or into the sewage system. Check with local officials regarding laws for disposing of unknown substances. Your school district also may have a waste management program to help teachers recognize hazardous waste and understand proper disposal. Possible sources of places that handle chemical waste include:

- Commercial chemical disposal companies in your area
- Some local industries
- Some colleges and universities have facilities for disposal available for use by schools.
- State and local conservation organizations
- Usable chemicals may be accepted by colleges, researchers, industry, or other schools. Contact the local American Chemical Society for suggestions. This method works best if direct communication is made with someone known to the person making the contact.
- You may be able to consolidate your waste with that of other local schools for more efficient disposal.
- **WARNING:** *Follow state and local regulations regarding the TRANSPORTATION of chemicals.*

**How to Dispose of Chemicals** There are several options for substance disposal, but each school or school district must make its own arrangements according to local restrictions of landfills, sewer systems, or other treatment works. **WARNING**: *Be sure you check your state and local regulations before you use any of the following methods.*

- carbon absorption
- oxidation/reduction
- precipitation and clarification
- biological treatment
- land disposal
- SOME hazardous wastes may be treated so that they are non- or less hazardous. For example, acids or bases may be carefully neutralized to a final pH range of 5–8 and then flushed down the drain with a 20-fold excess of water. Sodium bicarbonate is used to raise pH and 1 M of hydrocloric acid is used to lower pH. **WARNING**: *Pouring certain chemicals down the sink or other drains may interfere with chemicals used in water treatment processes.*
- Some waste disposal companies recycle chemicals and resell them.
- Recover laboratory wastes. Recovery of chemicals can be a learning tool for students, and may be presented as the final step in a chemistry experiment or as a project for more advanced chemistry students. The Internet, university chemistry departments, and the Environmental Protection Agency offer information about chemical recovery.

# Preparing Live Exhibits

Aquariums and terrariums are good ways to maintain organisms for class study. A variety of plants and animals grow well in them. Any glass container (4 L or larger) with a glass plate cover can be used as an aquarium or terrarium. Wash and rinse the container thoroughly before you use it.

Plants can be grown in the laboratory from seeds or cuttings. Bean plants, coleus, geraniums, and wandering jew are easily grown.

Instructions follow for preparing aquariums and terrariums and for growing plants.

## Aquariums

1. Place washed aquarium gravel on the bottom of the glass container to a depth of 4 cm.

2. Add aged tap water (water that has been standing open to the air for three days) to a depth of 5 cm above the gravel.

3. Anchor aquatic plants, such as eel grass, in the gravel.

4. Fill the aquarium by pouring aged tap water over a saucer to avoid disturbing the gravel on the bottom.

5. Let the aquarium stand for one day.

6. Add guppies, goldfish, snails, duckweed, and other organisms. (Recall that guppies are cannibalistic, so keep young and adults separated.)

7. Suspend a thermometer in the water so you can monitor the temperature. Maintain a temperature of 20–25°C. A lamp or sunny window can supply light and warmth.

8. Cover the aquarium.

9. Wedge a wooden splint between the cover and the top of the container to allow for air passage.

10. Add small amounts of high protein baby cereal or special fish food daily. Snails will eat any food the fish do not consume.

11. Keep the plants pruned so they do not fill the tank.

12. Keep tap water aging to replace any water lost by evaporation.

13. If green water develops in the aquarium, do not discard. It is an excellent source of food for other organisms.

## Terrariums

1. Place pebbles on the bottom of the glass container to a depth of 2 cm.

2. Add layers of 1 cm of clean sand and 3 cm of topsoil.

3. Place a layer of healthy green moss on top of the topsoil.

4. Plant several clusters of small ferns and liverworts. Lichens also can be added.

5. Place interesting rocks and driftwood in the terrarium.

6. Cover the terrarium.

7. Place the terrarium in filtered light.

8. Keep the plants moist by sprinkling with water occasionally. The pebble and sand layers allow for drainage. If water accumulates in the pebble layer, do not add more water.

Live Exhibits

**131**

# Plants

1. Mix equal parts of sand and topsoil. Place the mixture 5 cm deep in the bottom of a milk carton or plastic sandwich bag.

2. Plant seeds or cuttings from other plants.

3. Keep the soil moist.

4. Seeds should germinate within two weeks. Cuttings should root in two to four weeks. (Some cuttings can be rooted in water alone.)

5. Place coarse sand or pebbles in the bottom of pots for drainage.

6. Transplant the seedlings or rooted cuttings into the pots.

7. Water occasionally. Do not over water. Rotting stems and roots and yellow or brown leaves may indicate over watering.

8. Place the plants in a warm, lighted area where the air is moist. Leaf curling is a sign of too much heat. Dropping leaves indicate a lack of humidity.

9. Slow-release plant food should be added every two to three months to supply nutrients.

# Checking Facilities and Equipment

Surveying your facilities and knowing what you'll be working with is a very important step in managing the success and safety of your students. You'll need to have in mind the number of students in each class, how many labs you'll be teaching, and whether they will be earth science, physical science, or life science activities.

If you are not the only one using the science classroom and lab facilities, the survey of the facilities should be done as a team. If you have more than one laboratory available, you may wish to consider setting up each lab for a specific use. Savings can be realized if you set up earth science equipment in one lab, physical science equipment in another, and life science materials in a third.

You may find that a portable demonstration cart will add to your flexibility. See **Figure 1**. If each teacher has one, a teacher can move his or her cart as needed to either an earth, life, or physical science laboratory, or use it for demonstrations in a lecture situation. The carts also may be used for small group activities. These carts are available from scientific suppliers. They usually contain a work space, sink, gas torch or burner, water reservoir, and storage cabinet. **WARNING:** *Do NOT store hazardous materials in the cabinet.*

**Figure 1**

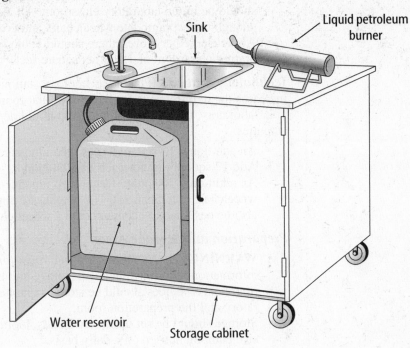

Sink

Liquid petroleum burner

Water reservoir

Storage cabinet

# Facilities Specifications

This section presents information on various aspects of school science buildings, such as recommended amounts of space for student work areas and fulfilling storage needs for a well-managed science classroom/lab. Basic specifications for built-in features for fire control and air quality are given as well.

## Space Requirements

Space requirements include a minimum amount of space for student work areas and room for separate storage and preparation areas.

*Student Work Areas* Generally, state regulations stipulate a certain amount of square footage per student per instruction level or a certain number of students per a 1,200-square foot laboratory. The net square footage includes exposed storage space, such as cabinets or shelving. The square footage does NOT include hallway space, storage closets, or preparation offices.

- At the middle and high school levels, there should be no more than 22 to 25 students per laboratory classroom of about 1,200 net square feet in area. This assumes that two of the students are special needs students.
- If there are three special needs students in the class, only 20 students should be in the laboratory classroom. All aisles and exits should be wide enough to accommodate wheelchairs and crutches.
- At the elementary level, there should be no more than 22 students per laboratory classroom of 1,200 net square feet.

*Technology Stations* Placing technology stations in the classroom laboratory increases the requirements for the size of that room. If you add such stations to your laboratory, the number of students should decrease accordingly for the lab activities.

- An additional 15 square feet is recommended per computer station.
- Add 12 square feet for each VCR station.
- An additional 20 square feet is recommended for a station if it is to meet wheelchair specifications. The height of a special needs station should also be designed to accommodate a wheel chair.

## Preparation and Storage Areas

- **WARNING:** *Do NOT use a storage room for preparation.* See p. 127 for information regarding chemical storage and handling.
- Materials resources should be stored separately from the classroom laboratory and the preparation room.
- Storage should be set up for chemicals, biological specimens, and expensive equipment used on a daily basis.
- Odd-sized items, such as distillation units, skeletons, centrifuges, carts, microwaves, and so forth, need to be considered when planning your storage rooms.
- Storage rooms should be locked to prevent unauthorized use of equipment, especially such items as syringes, scalpels, lasers, microscopes, balances, and anything else that is expensive to replace or could lead to accidents.
- In earthquake-prone areas, fragile equipment should be attached to the lab bench. Velcro straps are recommended if the equipment is moved often. Otherwise, a clear silicone sealant placed on the feet of the equipment that adheres to the bench may be used.

- Compressed gas cylinder supports should be securely fastened, preferably by bolting them to a solid wall or a bench. If restraint straps are used, they MUST be nonflammable. **WARNING:** *Turn-screw compression clamps are inadequate in earthquake-prone areas.*

## Fire Control Features

In the event of fire, science classrooms must meet minimum requirements set forth by the National Fire Protection Association (NFPA) and your local fire officials. These include such requirements as:

- You MUST have two clearly marked emergency exits for each science room, preparation room, and equipment/materials storage room. One of the exits in a ground floor room may be a window if it is large enough for an adult to escape through.
- Fire extinguishers should be placed at eye level at every exit. See p. 140 regarding specifications for fire extinguishers.
- All rooms should have a sprinkler system.
- All rooms should have smoke alarms.
- A general fire alarm system throughout the building is required.
- Fire drill procedures MUST be posted and practiced.
- A fire blanket should be located at eye level near each fire extinguisher. It should be clearly marked and accessible. (See p. 140 for more information on fire blankets.)
- All utilities should have a master cut-off control switch. These should be easily accessible by teachers but not so handy to students. The controls should be clearly labeled as to the room location and type of utility.
- **WARNING:** *Stairways and hallways must NOT be used as storage areas.*
- **WARNING:** *NEVER block access to exits, emergency equipment, control switches, and so forth.*

## Electrical Systems

Fires in the classroom laboratory commonly result from misuse of electrical power and equipment. The following precautions can eliminate such fires.

- Two duplex outlets per station are generally recommended plus two duplex outlets per non-lab station wall.
- Use only one hot plate per outlet.
- Use a surge protector with each computer.
- Avoid using extension cords. If you must use extension cords, they must be heavy-duty and NOT be in the path of students moving from one area to another.
- All electrical outlets should be properly wired and grounded.
- Outlets should accommodate a 3-pronged plug.
- Ground-fault circuit interrupters (GFCI) should be installed on all outlets.
- Outlets should be located away from sinks or other water sources and above floor level. If lab tables have both water and electrical resources, the electrical outlets MUST have GFCI devices.
- Test all outlets to be sure the wiring is correct.
- Use small dry cells in place of DC lines.
- Use only 110-volt Underwriters Laboratory (UL) approved equipment (See pp. 142–144 for more information about investigation equipment specifications.)

## Air Quality Control

Proper ventilation systems contribute to a safe environment for you and your students. These systems must vary depending upon the use of the classroom and laboratories involved. The following basic information should provide a minimum of protection. Other information may be obtained from American National Standards Institute (ANSI) Z9.5.

### Science Classroom/Laboratory and Preparation Room Ventilation

- The ventilation system should allow a rate of **four** changes of air per hour.
- Vents should go to the outside and be placed away from air intake ducts.
- The system should be separate from the building's system and from any other science classroom's system.
- Ductwork should be lined with a material that does not corrode.
- Rooms should have exhaust fans designed for rapid (five min) venting of smoke or bad odors created during an activity. These fans should have a manual switch. If the fans are mounted on the wall, fan guards are recommended.
- **WARNING:** *Should the air quality system fail for any reason (power outage, mechanical breakdown, and so forth), the laboratory MUST be placed off limits until the system is restored.*

### Storage Room Ventilation

- Chemical storage room ventilation systems should allow a rate of **six** changes of air per hour.
- Vents should go to the outside (preferably above the roof) and be placed away from air intake ducts.

### Flammable Materials Cabinets

- **WARNING**: *These cabinets should NOT be vented.*

### Fume Hoods

- Fume hoods should be available for any activity that uses or generates vapors or gases.
- Fume hoods should be installed according to the following basic criteria:
  - Fume hoods should be placed at least 10 feet from doors, windows, or vents to avoid interference from airflow caused by other vents/exhaust systems.
  - Fume hoods should be vented the same as the main ventilation system—to the outside above the roof and away from air intake ducts.
  - Fume hoods should NOT be placed along main traffic aisles.
  - If more than one hood is installed, there should be at least two feet between the hoods.
  - Fit hoods with traps, scrubbers, or condensers to collect wastes to keep them from being released into the atmosphere.
  - The sash level should be marked for a draw of 80 to 120 linear feet per minute of air movement. Mark the appropriate closure point for times when the sash must be partially closed during an activity. (See **Figure 2** on the next page.)
- Test the efficiency of fume hoods periodically by checking air movement—it should be inward and upward in the hood. You can measure fume hood velocity with an air flow meter. Face velocities should be in the range of 60 to 100 cubic feet per minute.

# Advantages of Small-Scale Chemistry

Several advantages result from scaling down the amount of chemicals used in investigations. See pp. 30–34 for some of the devices needed for using very small amounts of chemicals.

### Economic Savings

Reduced costs result from having to buy smaller quantities of materials. While buying a larger amount may make the unit price smaller, the total amount needed for small-scale chemistry will be greatly reduced, thus resulting in a savings. Microscale glassware also will bring savings after the initial investment is made. For example, a microplate with 64 wells costs less than 64 test tubes and the test-tube racks needed to hold 64 test tubes.

### Safety

Using smaller amounts of chemicals results in smaller amounts of toxic vapors being released, smaller spills needing to be cleaned up, and smaller amounts of vapors and materials contributing to fire hazards.

### Less Storage Space

Microscale glassware and other equipment take up much less space than macroscale items. Needing smaller amounts of chemicals and other substances also saves shelf space in storage rooms and cabinets.

### Less Waste

Less hazardous waste is a great advantage to the environment and also a savings in the cost of disposing of hazardous waste. (See p. 129.)

### Time Savings

Using very small amounts of materials means that reaction times are reduced. For example, it takes a much shorter time to heat 20 mL to a desired temperature than it does to heat 200 mL.

# Safety Equipment Specifications

The same general guidelines for investigation equipment apply to safety equipment. (See p. 142.) Safety equipment can be grouped according to use. One group of equipment is used for personal protection as a precaution. Another group contains the equipment needed to deal with accidents if they occur. Appropriate use of this equipment can be found in the section entitled "Responding to Emergencies" on pp. 91–104.

## Personal Protection Equipment

Personal protection equipment MUST be worn if there is a chance of exposure to harmful substances. Some school districts require that you don goggles and aprons before entering the laboratory.

*Eyewear* Several types of eyewear are available. They are NOT the same. The type of eyewear worn MUST match the activity.

- *Safety goggles* are required for all lab activities, in the laboratory or out. Check your local and state regulations for the preferred code. This code will appear on the frames and lenses.
- Safety goggles should be large enough to protect and form a seal around the eyes. They should also be able to form a seal around eyeglasses without affecting the eye correction afforded by the eyeglasses. **WARNING:** *Contact lenses can trap chemicals (even vapors) against the cornea and cause damage.*
- Safety goggles are available that are designed to protect the eyes from liquid splashes, vapors, dusts, and impact.
- Face shields can provide additional protection when used *with* some form of safety eyeware.
- *Laser goggles* are rated for the wavelength and power of a particular laser. (See p. 143.) One type of goggles is NOT automatically usable with any laser. **WARNING:** *Chemical safety goggles are NOT suitable for work with lasers.*
- All eyewear MUST be sterilized before reuse if the person has an infection or if the eyewear is to be used by another person. (See pp. 84–85.)
- **WARNING:** *NO devices have been approved to protect the eyes against direct viewing of the sun.*

*Gloves* Gloves should be used to protect the hands against heat, sharp objects, chemicals, body fluids, and so forth. **WARNING:** The same type of glove will NOT protect the hands against all hazards. Certain gloves can dissolve when they come in contact with solvent. The glove type should match the activity being performed. Suppliers often include in their catalogs a list rating the effectiveness of certain materials in protecting against particular substances. Or, refer to the manufacturer's MSDS (see p. 117) if there is a question regarding which type of glove to use with a certain chemical.

- *Polyethylene gloves* protect the hands against light corrosives and irritants.
- *Latex gloves* protect against biological materials. They should be changed as soon as they are soiled. (See p. 89) **WARNING:** *Some people may have an allergic reaction to latex.*
- *Hypoallergenic latex gloves,* while more expensive than regular latex, are available. Cotton gloves also may be worn beneath latex, neoprene, and nitrile gloves to protect against irritation.

- *Natural rubber gloves* help protect against electrical shock and light corrosives.
- *Neoprene gloves* provide protection against mineral acids and alcohols.
- *Nitrile gloves* are resistant against solvents, punctures, and abrasion.
- *Oven mitts* should be used when dealing with heat sources and heated materials. **WARNING:** *Asbestos gloves are NOT recommended. Asbestos is a known carcinogen.*

### Clothing/Body Protectors
Laboratory aprons and coats are worn to protect the skin and clothing from spilled materials that might be hazardous. Protective clothing comes in many types of material.

- Aprons and lab coats made with multiple layers offer protection from permeation.
- **WARNING:** *Check to be sure that the protective material is flame retardant.*
- Aprons should have bibs that tie closely to the lower part of the neck. They should cover the body at least to the knees and be worn over clothing that covers the arms.

### Face Masks
Face masks offer protection against dust, allergens, and vapors. Some people are allergic to odors that may not be classified as hazardous to most people. Masks are available that offer varying degrees of protection, depending upon the need.

### Waste Disposal Containers
Every lab should be equipped with the proper containers for the various kinds of waste that might be produced. For example, biohazard sharp objects must be placed in a puncture-proof container. Waste containers should be labeled properly and placed in a location that is convenient but out of the way of heavy traffic. Waste containers require proper storage and ventilation. See pp. 127 and 136.

## Accident Response Equipment

This section deals with the specifications for accident response equipment. See pp. 93–94 for procedures for using the equipment.

### Eyewash Stations
An eyewash station MUST be available where chemicals are used, including classrooms and preparation rooms. An eyewash station should be reachable within 10 s (or 25 feet) by anyone who has been splashed. Some basic guidelines include the following:

- Plumbed fixtures are recommended, possibly as part of safety showers. **WARNING:** *Squeeze bottles are NOT recommended. They do not contain enough solution to be effective and can only treat one eye at a time.*
- The eyewash device should wash both eyes at the same time and allow for hands to be free to hold the eyelids open.
- The station should supply an instant, gentle flow of water continuously for 15 min (at least 3.0 gal/min at 30 psi).
- Water temperature should be in the range of 32–35°C (90–95°F) to lessen shock to tissues.
- The eyewash station should accommodate people in wheelchairs.
- The eyewash device should be flushed for 5 min each week to remove any contaminants.
- Portable eyewash tanks are available but are NOT recommended except when the stationary eyewash unit is not functioning. Follow-up care should be provided as the portable tanks deliver only about 8 gallons of water.

*Safety Showers* Some basic guidelines for safety showers follow:

- Permanent plumbing fixtures are recommended.
- A deluge shower is needed for major spills; a hand-held sprayer with a 6-foot hose may be used for minor spills and for eyewashes if a permanent eyewash station is not functioning.
- A safety shower should deliver at least 20 gallons of water per min at 30 psi.
- Water temperature should be within the range of 15–35°C (60–95°F).
- Safety showers should be NO more than 10 s away from the spill.
- Safety showers should have control valves that are easy to turn on and that stay on without the use of hands.
- Safety showers should be large enough to accommodate both the injured person (in a wheelchair if necessary) and the adult assisting with the emergency.
- Safety showers should be flushed weekly to be sure they are working properly and to eliminate any contaminants.

*Fire Blankets* Fire blankets made of specially treated wool should be available in all science laboratories where hazardous chemicals are used or stored. **WARNING:** *Fire blankets made of asbestos are NOT recommended; asbestos is a known carcinogen.*

*Fire Extinguishers* Using proper equipment is extremely important in fighting fires. There are four classes of fire and they each involve a different method of extinction. Fire extinguishers are labeled for the class of fire they are to be used on. **WARNING:** *NEVER use fire extinguishers that contain carbon tetrachloride—this toxic substance can form phosgene, which is even more toxic than carbon tetrachloride.*

**Table 1**

| Fire Class | Methods of Extinction | | Precautions |
|---|---|---|---|
| **Class A:** ordinary combustibles (paper, wood) | Water | Dry chemical class ABC fire extinguisher | *Water should never be used on Class B, C, or D fires* |
| **Class B:** flammable liquids (acetone, alcohol, ethers, grease) | | Class B or dry chemical Class ABC fire extinguisher | |
| **Class C:** electrical or static charges | | Class C or dry chemical Class ABC fire extinguisher | |
| **Class D:** combustible metals (magnesium, potassium, sodium) | Dry, clean sand | Class D fire extinguisher | *Dry, clean sand is suitable for small fires; NEVER use water on flammable metals–some of them react violently with water* |

- Fire extinguishers must be located in each science classroom, laboratory, storage room, and preparation area.
- Fire extinguishers should be selected for the area to be covered. UL labels on the extinguishers define their capacities. A UL label of 2A:40B:C means the extinguisher can cover 2 square feet of a Class A fire or 40 square feet of a Class B fire, or may be used for a Class C fire.
- Fire extinguishers should be checked periodically and maintained at full charge.

***Materials for Chemical-Spill Cleanup*** Cleanup materials can be items that quickly absorb liquids or substances that neutralize an acid or caustic spill. Cleanup materials are available from chemical supply companies.

- Absorbent materials include fire blankets; spill pillows; spill mats or pads; clean, dry sand; and clean cat litter. Special spill control kits are needed for mercury. These include sprays to reduce mercury vapor, special sponges, and safe storage containers for the waste.
- You also will need an inert-bristle broom (such as polypropylene), plastic or metal dustpans (depending on the reactivity of the substance spilled), and large, sealable plastic bags. (See guidelines for cleanup procedures on p. 89.)

***First Aid Kits*** First aid supplies should be kept readily at hand. Immediate aid then can be given while waiting for the school nurse or emergency squads. At a minimum, supplies should include the following (see pp. 94–97 for first aid procedures):

- *Recommended items for first aid kits:*
  - disposable gloves (latex or plastic)
  - antiseptic
  - disinfectant
  - bleach (at time needed, prepare a solution of 1 part bleach to 10 parts water)
  - disposable towels
  - sterile gauze for covering large wounds
  - medical tape
  - scissors
  - adhesive bandages for covering small wounds
  - plastic bags for holding contaminated waste
- *Items NOT recommended for first aid kits*
  - iodine **WARNING:** *It can cause tissue damage.*
  - ice pack compress **WARNING:** *Swelling of soft tissues should be examined by a physician.*
  - ammonia inhalants **WARNING:** If person is unconscious, get help immediately.
  - tourniquet **WARNING:** *Use pressure until medical assistance is available.*

# Safety Requirements for Investigation Equipment

Following some basic precautions regarding laboratory equipment can greatly reduce common hazards. See pp. 18–22 for safe techniques in the use of investigation equipment and materials.

## General Equipment Guidelines

- Keep manufacturer's instructions for equipment at hand for proper usage techniques as well as safety precautions.
- Protect equipment from dust, humidity, and extreme temperatures, especially electronic equipment and microscopes.
- In earthquake-prone areas, equipment should be clamped to the table top.
- All electrical equipment should be 110-volt approved by Underwriters Laboratory or other equivalent. All outlets, surge protectors, and cords should be well above floor level.
- Work surfaces should NOT have cracks or areas inaccessible to cleaning.
- All work surfaces should be resistant to water, heat, and chemicals.
- Noise levels should be controlled. Sustained noises above 80 dBA can cause or lead to hearing damage. Guidelines regarding exposure to noise are shown in **Table 2.**

**Table 2**

| Sound Level Limits | | | |
|---|---|---|---|
| Sound level (dBA) | Exposure limit | Typical source | Resulting hearing damage (after exposure limit) |
| 150 | 0 s | Jet plane taking off | Ruptured ear drum |
| 120 | 7 min 30 s | Chain saw, live rock music | Pain and serious damage |
| 110 | 30 min | Power saw, rock music | Serious damage |
| 105 | 1 h | Snow blower | Serious damage |
| 100 | 2 h | Woodworking shop | Serious damage |
| 95 | 4 h | Electric drill | Serious damage |
| 90 | 8 h | Tractor | Damage |
| 85 | 8 h | Electric shaver | Possible damage |
| 80 | None | Mini-bike | Possible damage |

## Specific Guidelines for Commonly Used Equipment
### Heat Sources

- Hot plates with a flat surface (NOT coils) are recommended for heat sources. **WARNING:** *Hot plates stay hot after they are unplugged or turned off. Some hot plates have warning lights to show they are hot.* Be sure that you have an adequate number of outlets for the hot plates (one outlet per hot plate).
- A high temperature burner with a grid produces excellent results for bending glass. See p. 21 for techniques for bending glass.
- If your laboratory is supplied with gas burners, they MUST be filled with the appropriate type of gas. A manual central cut-off valve should be accessible to the teacher. **WARNING:** *NEVER use open flames when a flammable solvent is in the same room.* (See pp. 18–19.)
- Alcohol burners are NOT recommended. **WARNING:** *Alcohol burners are potentially explosive in the event of a fire. If you must use an alcohol burner, see p. 18 regarding proper procedures for doing so.*

***Thermometers*** Digital thermometers are recommended. Some cities now prohibit the sale of mercury thermometers. If a mercury thermometer is required for accuracy, use one with a coating that helps contain the mercury even if the glass is broken. **WARNING:** *Exposure to mercury can cause paralysis and developmental problems in small children.* (See p. 83 regarding disposal of mercury thermometers and cleanup of mercury spills.)

***Refrigerators*** Cold storage is often recommended for certain materials, such as biological specimens and flammable solvents. Specifications for laboratory refrigerators include the following:

- An explosion-proof refrigerator is recommended for storage of flammable materials. These have modified internal wiring and sealed motors and switches to prevent sparks. **WARNING:** *Control switches and defroster heaters in a home refrigerator can spark which may ignite flammable materials and cause explosions.*
- A refrigerator used for storing radioactive materials MUST have the standard symbol for radioactivity on the door. The refrigerator should be checked periodically for radioactive contamination. **WARNING:** *NEVER store food in a science storage refrigerator.*
- In earthquake-prone areas, refrigerators should have secure closing devices. Older magnetic locks have not always proved effective during earthquakes.

***Glassware*** Most injuries in the classroom laboratory are cuts that result from glassware breakage. Using the proper kinds of glassware can greatly reduce the chance of injuries. (See pp. 83 and 89 for safe techniques and cleanup procedures.)

- Glassware should be heat resistant.
- Glassware also should offer resistance to chemicals and accidental breakage.

### Batteries

- Alkaline or dry-cell batteries are recommended for classroom use.
- Lead storage batteries should be used only when a larger DC current is needed. **WARNING:** *Lead storage batteries contain liquid sulfuric acid and have the ability to deliver sufficient current to cause wire insulation to ignite.*

*Lasers* Lasers are classified by the Bureau of Radiological Health according to the amount of power they emit—Class I to Class IV. Those recommended for secondary schools are Class II and III-A lasers. **WARNING:** *Even low-powered lasers may cause eye damage.* (See p. 138 for the proper type of goggles for use with lasers.)

*Acceleration Models* Two common types of acceleration models are rockets and steam engines. Following safety standards can reduce hazard levels, which include the possibility of hearing damage.

- *Rockets* Some common recommendations for rockets include the following.
  - Rockets should be made of lightweight materials.
  - The rocket, including the engine, should NOT weigh more than 453 g. The engine should NOT have more than 133 g of propellant.
  - The propellant should be a solid propellant, and only factory-made engines should be used. **WARNING:** *Students should NOT rework or reload the engines; an explosion could result.*
  - Remote-controlled launches in open areas are recommended. Students should be at least 15 feet from the rocket.

- *Engines* Steam engines with solid fuel burners are recommended for classroom laboratories. **WARNING:** *Alcohol fuel is NOT recommended. Pure alcohol burns with an invisible flame. If additional alcohol is added to the burner because it appears the flame has gone out, vapors and the stock can of alcohol may be ignited.*